CONTENTS

The Dog Who Saved

and other
True Animal Tales

Allan Zullo

Scholastic Inc.

New York   Toronto   London   Auckland   Sydney
Mexico City   New Delhi   Hong Kong   Buenos Aires

To my grandson Jack Manausa, with hopes that the holiday
spirit shines within him every day of the year
—A.Z.

ISBN-13: 978-0-545-04643-5
ISBN-10: 0-545-04643-2

30 29 28 27   16 17 18/0

Printed in the U.S.A.
First Scholastic printing, November 2008

Paws
to Remember

Don't you just love the holidays? In the days leading up to Christmas, Hanukkah, or Kwanzaa, you may be filled with the happy anticipation of tearing open presents and tasting all sorts of yummy treats. You sing and listen to favorite holiday songs while decorating your home in festive colors. And you join loved ones in family traditions that have been passed down from generation to generation. It's a joyous season whose memories last a lifetime.

But kids and grown-ups aren't the only ones who make holiday memories. Pets do, too. In the following pages, you will read true stories of dogs, cats, birds, and other animals who turned the holidays into a season never to be forgotten. Each story is based on a true-life event, although dialogue has been added and several scenes have been dramatized. In certain cases, names have been changed.

Some of the accounts in this book spotlight the mischievous and naughty side of family pets. Other stories feature heart-warming moments that illustrate the animals' loving natures. And many of these tales reveal how these remarkable pets can teach us some of the true meanings of the holidays.

The Dog Who Saved Christmas

I'm going to drown, thought Karen Webster. *Of all days, I'm going to die on Christmas Eve.*

Karen had accidentally fallen into her family's swimming pool and now stood helplessly at the bottom in the deep end. The overweight, middle-aged woman could barely move because her soaked layers of winter clothes and hiking boots kept her anchored near the bottom. But for a woman about to drown, she felt a strange calmness, as though resigned to accepting her fate. She could neither save herself nor count on anyone else to rescue her. Her husband and two daughters were out delivering Christmas presents to needy families.

How horrible it will be for Frank and the kids to find me dead. Why did it have to be like this? Why did it have to be on Christmas Eve?

She was almost out of air. Looking up toward the surface, she could barely make out the wavy yellow form of the family dog racing back and forth along the edge of the pool, barking frantically.

"Mom, this is soooo heartbreaking," moaned twelve-year-old Emily. "The dogs are so cute. I wish we could take all of them home with us."

"Yeah, Mom," said ten-year-old Ellie. "I don't know which one to choose because I'll feel bad for the rest that we couldn't pick."

"I know it's hard, but think of it this way: We're going to make a difference in the life of one homeless dog," said Karen. She was walking with her daughters through the large kennel area of an animal shelter near their home in Ocala, Florida. They had agreed to get an adult dog rather than a puppy because they wanted a pet whose temperament was known and who was already house-broken. They also were hoping to find a Labrador retriever, because the girls had grown up with a Lab named Jingles until his death a few months earlier from old age.

Emily was the first to spot her — a two-year-old female yellow Lab with a shiny coat that matched her eyes. Shelter worker Vicki Peters opened the cage door and let the dog out. The canine immediately greeted Karen and the girls with a little hop and a tail that kept beating against their legs as she weaved her way from one to the other.

"She deserves a loving home," said Vicki. "She's had a hard life. Her owners kept her chained outside. They abused her and didn't always feed her or keep her sheltered. They had her on a chained collar for so long, it became imbedded in her skin while she grew.

"Neighbors felt sorry for the dog and would sneak into the backyard when the owners were gone and give her food. One neighbor offered to take her off the owners' hands, but they refused. They claimed they kept her to scare off burglars, but it's hard to see how she could scare anyone when she was chained. Besides, Labs don't make good guard dogs because they're so gentle.

"The neighbor couldn't stand it anymore and called us. We went over to the owners' house and talked to them. At first, they denied any abuse. But it was obvious. The dog was skinny and had the collar stuck in her neck. It took a while, but finally we convinced them to give us the dog.

"When we brought her back to the shelter, we had to use steel clippers to cut off the collar. It took weeks for her wounds to heal. We put her on a special diet and fed her five times a day so she could gain some weight.

"She was extremely shy at first, but within a few days she was playing with the other dogs. We had her in a foster home for several weeks to see how she handled living with children — and she's wonderful with them. She's turned into a sweet dog. She would make an excellent family pet."

Watching the way the Lab was interacting with them, Karen and her daughters agreed this dog was the one. When they brought her home, they named her Cinnamon. The once-abused Lab thrived in the Websters' home, getting more love in a single day than she had received in the first two years of her life.

That's not to say she was a perfect dog. Far from it. Sometimes she would jump in the pool, get out, roll around in the garden, and gallop through the open patio door, leaving a trail of muddy paw prints on the tile floor. She also would leap into the water and splash the girls whenever they were floating on their inflatable rafts. Once, she tried to crawl onto their rafts, only to puncture holes with her claws.

The family lost count of the number of times her wagging, powerful tail knocked over a can of soda that had been sitting on the coffee table in the family room. And no one could tally how often Cinnamon tried to snatch the remains of a sandwich left unattended on the kitchen table.

But all was forgiven, especially after the crisis that Karen and the girls faced in early December 2001. Their local church had raised nearly two thousand dollars to spend on Christmas gifts for the children of ten needy families. Karen was given the money so she and the girls could buy the presents. On the morning of their scheduled shopping spree, they were getting ready when Karen bellowed in anguish, "I can't find the money!"

"You're joking, right?" said Emily.

"No," Karen declared. "I've lost the black leather moneybag that held all the money. I've looked everywhere. Girls, I need you to help me find it."

"Don't panic, Mom. Just retrace your steps. When did you last have it?"

"Pastor Richardson handed it to me last night at the church hall. I put it in my coat pocket and then drove home. When I walked in the house, I was bombarded by everyone. Emily, you insisted I play the piano so you could practice your solo at the school holiday show. Ellie, you dragged me into your room to help wrap a present. And then I helped Dad chase Cinnamon, who was all wet from jumping in the pool. With all that going on, I didn't think any more about the money. I assumed the moneybag was still in my coat pocket this morning, but it's not there. I've looked everywhere."

"Don't worry, Mom," said Ellie. "We'll find it."

"What am I going to do?" Karen fretted. She slumped in a chair at the kitchen table and buried her head in her hands. "I feel sick to my stomach. The church entrusted me with the money and I lost it. If I don't find it, I'll have to come up with two thousand dollars out of our savings account. I can't let the church or those needy children down. What a terrible Christmas this is going to be for us."

The three of them searched everywhere in the house and then combed the yard until . . .

"Mom! Mom!" Ellie shouted. "We found it! We found the money!"

"What? Where?"

"Actually, Cinnamon found it," said Emily. "Look."

The Lab was sitting down in front of Karen's car in the driveway, wagging her tail, and holding the missing moneybag in her mouth. Karen ran over to her, took the moneybag, zipped it open, and counted the money. She let out a big *whew* and said, "Oh, thank goodness. It's all here."

Ellie hugged Cinnamon and said, "Way to go, girl!"

"Where did she find it?" Karen asked.

"We were in the driveway walking to your car to check inside again when Cinnamon came over from the passenger's side,"

Emily explained. "She was sniffing the grass by the edge of the driveway and then she picked up the moneybag."

"I think I know what happened," said Karen. "When I got out of the car last night, I went around to the passenger's side to bring in the clothes I had picked up at the dry cleaners. My cell phone rang and I reached in my coat pocket to answer it, and that's when the moneybag must have fallen out."

She bent over and gave Cinnamon a big smooch on the nose. "Oh, you are a wonderful dog. You just saved Christmas for a bunch of families."

For the next week, Karen gave the dog extra treats — even grilling a hamburger especially for her — because "nothing is too good for my Cinnamon."

After completing their shopping spree, Karen and the girls wrapped toys, clothes, and games for the needy children. "This is turning into a great Christmas," said Ellie.

"Yeah, thanks to Cinnamon," Emily said.

Shopping for the disadvantaged kids had put the family in the true holiday spirit. In the afternoon of December 24, Frank and the girls delivered the gifts to the families while Karen stayed home to prepare their special Christmas Eve dinner of pork roast, sweet potatoes, green-bean casserole, and pumpkin pie. She was glad to remain inside because it was unseasonably cold for central Florida.

When she heard the weather forecast on the radio calling for temperatures to dip into the mid-twenties overnight, she decided to cover her delicate plants around the pool area before it got dark. Karen, who hated to feel cold, was wearing sweatpants over leggings and a flannel shirt under a Florida State sweatshirt. Before stepping outside, she put on a fleece-lined winter jacket and hiking boots and then gathered several old sheets.

A blustery breeze made the overcast day seem much colder than the forty-degree temperature of the air. "We need to move south for the winter," she joked to Cinnamon.

While the dog followed her around the patio area, Karen spread sheets over the flowers to protect them from frost. She was draping a sheet on her small potted orange tree next to the pool when a gust lifted the sheet and blew it in her face. She backpedaled, lost her balance, and toppled backward into the pool, plunging into the deep end. She sank quickly and was six feet under the surface when her feet hit the bottom.

Karen, who was not a good swimmer, frantically tried to claw at the water, hoping to work her way to the top. But she could hardly budge because her layers of clothing were soaked and weighed her down, restricting her movements. She was ready to give up. *I can't believe I'm going to drown here in my own swimming pool,* she thought. *What a horrible time to die — right before Christmas.*

Above her, she saw the blurry outline of Cinnamon, running back and forth along the edge of the pool. Through the water, she heard the muffled sounds of the dog's frantic barking.

I can't hold out much longer. As Karen began to pray, she saw a big splash above her. *Cinnamon!* The dog-paddling Lab circled around the woman's head for a few seconds, then stopped and dipped her hindquarters. *Closer, closer. I'm almost out of breath.* Reaching up, Karen grabbed the end of the dog's sturdy tail — the tail that had knocked down Karen's one-year-old niece the previous week and overturned a bowl of chips on the coffee table a day later.

But today, the tail that had brought trouble for Cinnamon was now a lifeline to the person she loved. When Karen clutched the tail, the dog began swimming with all her might, towing the drowning woman toward the shallow end. It wasn't easy. The 70-pound dog was pulling about 265 pounds — nearly four times her own weight. Cinnamon never stopped paddling as she dragged her owner closer to the shallow end.

By now, Karen was out of air and her lungs felt on fire. Her body was protesting until she could no longer keep her mouth clenched. Just as she started to take in water, she felt her feet touch the shallow end and, with one desperate effort, she thrust her head above the surface and gulped in fresh air. But because she had swallowed water, too, she hacked, coughed, and sputtered for several minutes.

I'm not going to die!

With Cinnamon's help, the woman struggled to the stairs and collapsed, retching and coughing up the last of the water that she had consumed. Cinnamon stayed by her side, licking her face until she had regained her strength.

As Karen staggered out of the pool, Frank and the girls arrived. They rushed over to the soaked, shivering woman and helped her inside. Exhausted from her ordeal, Karen explained to them what had happened. When she finished, she said, "If Cinnamon hadn't come to my rescue, I would have drowned."

The wet dog rubbed against her legs and gave a little *ruff.*

"Your heroism was the best Christmas present I ever received," Karen said.

Emily threw her arms around Cinnamon and added, "Imagine that, Cinnamon. You're the dog who saved Christmas — twice!"

The Winged Wonder

The reflection of the flames from the bonfires danced across the wide eyes of eight-year-old Theodore "Theo" Landry. "Uncle Eddie, I've never seen anything like this before," he said in openmouthed amazement.

In the misty night of Christmas Eve in 1901, the horse-drawn wagon clip-clopped on a road along the levee of the Mississippi River outside New Orleans. Sitting next to his uncle, who held the reins, Theo marveled at the dozens of teepee-shaped bonfires that blazed in glorious shades of oranges, reds, and yellows. The fires lit the way for families in decorated carriages and well-dressed people heading toward holiday gatherings.

It was the first time Eddie Landry had seen his nephew smile since the tragic accident two months earlier.

"Why are there so many bonfires, Uncle Eddie?"

"For Papa Noel, of course."

"Who's Papa Noel?"

Theo's bald, roly-poly uncle scratched a bushy eyebrow and replied, "The Santa Claus of New Orleans, yes sirree. He don't own a sleigh 'cause it'd sink in the bayou. Instead he moves 'bout in a pirogue [pronounced pee-rowg] – a flat-bottomed canoe that gets 'round in the deepest swamp. And he has no need for reindeer, no sirree. His pirogue is pulled by eight tame alligators.

"Now, as you can plainly see, it can get foggy here. So all us mist-dwellers, moon-lovers, and gumbo-eaters wanna make sure Papa Noel can find his way to our homes. So we light these big bonfires along the levee on Christmas Eve so he can see where he's goin'."

As they entered New Orleans, Theo gazed in awe at the hundreds of flickering candles illuminating the park squares. The tiny flames cast a glow on the faces of the men, women, and children who were singing Christmas carols.

"I wish my mama and daddy were here to see this beautiful place," Theo said.

"They most surely are here, boy. They're lookin' down from heaven."

Theo didn't say anything. He missed his parents terribly since their untimely deaths back in his hometown of Kansas City. The skinny lad ran his fingers along his bulky metal leg braces and thought of all the "if only's" that had changed his life forever. If only there hadn't been a gas leak. If only his father hadn't lit a cigarette. If only the explosion hadn't killed his parents. If only he could have been there to save them. If only he hadn't been in the hospital at the time for another surgery on his deformed legs.

The rickety wagon entered an African-American neighborhood crammed with dozens of long but narrow wooden houses. Stopping in front of a red one on the corner, Eddie announced, "Here we are. This here's home for me and your aunt Maddie. And now it's yours, too."

Eddie helped Theo down from the wagon and handed him his cane. Despite his stiff, braced legs, the boy managed to climb the three steps to the small front porch. Suddenly, the door swung open, revealing a cheery, heavyset woman in a large-flowered dress. "Hallelujah, you're here!" shouted Aunt Maddie. She threw her chubby arms around Theo and gave him a warm kiss on each cheek. "Come on in, child. Why, I haven't seen you since you were eye-high to a crawdaddy. You must be tuckered out from your trip."

"I am a little tired, ma'am."

"And probably hungry, too. Well, you've come to the right place, 'cause your aunt Maddie is gonna fatten you up."

Maddie was an exceptional baker in great demand by the well-to-do of New Orleans, especially at this time of year. For the holidays, she made pound cakes and jelly cakes, mince pies and apple pies, and desserts made with pralines and dragées (sugar-coated almonds). Her specialty: melt-in-your-mouth petit fours (layers of sponge cake and buttercream topped with icing).

One of her best customers was Mrs. Simone Sudier, a high-society patron of the arts who had a heart of gold and loved to donate money to worthy causes. She and her wealthy husband, Jacques, lived on ritzy Esplanade Avenue in a gorgeous mansion cared for by a dozen servants and several handymen, one of whom was Eddie.

Maddie and Eddie's house consisted of four rooms all in a row — a living room, two bedrooms, and a kitchen in the back — and no hallway. "Pretty nice, huh?" Eddie said to Theo. "We even have a bathroom off the kitchen."

"I've never seen a house like this," said Theo.

"If you open up all the doors, you can fire a shotgun clean through from the front and out the back door without hittin' a thing," Eddie said. "That's why they call this kinda place a shotgun house."

It took a while before Theo settled into a new life with his loving aunt and uncle, who had no children of their own. Despite their lack of parenting experience, Eddie and Maddie gave him comfort, encouragement, and sometimes a gentle kick in the rear whenever he needed it most.

Theo's biggest problem was school. He hated it. Actually, he loved learning. It was the bullying he couldn't stand. Many of the kids made fun of his leg braces and his Midwestern accent. They called him Crip — short for cripple — or Lead Legs. One bully, Marquez Jackson, who was ten but looked and acted older, liked to kick the cane out from under Theo and then count how many seconds it took the boy to get up.

It's not that Theo didn't have any friends. He had a few. But they were too afraid to stand up for him, so they said nothing whenever Theo was tormented. And so Theo continued to suffer at school.

"Don't pay them no mind," Aunt Maddie urged him. "Those

bullies are just cowards. They have to pick on someone to cover up their own weaknesses. You stay strong, Theo, and ignore them."

He tried, but because of his small size, mild manner, and physical disability, he was an easy target. Months of ridicule, teasing, and pranks had turned Theo into a brooding, unhappy boy prone to snapping at his teacher and his aunt and uncle, too. What little self-esteem he had was overpowered by an anger boiling inside him.

One day after school in early December 1902, Marquez Jackson swiped the boy's cane and lodged it in the crook of a branch twenty feet up in a magnolia tree. Theo was seething but didn't say a word. Instead, while the bully and a throng of students looked on in amusement, Theo began inching his way up the tree. Grunting and groaning, the skinny kid showed unexpected strength that surprised everyone, including himself. When Theo reached his cane, Marquez shouted, "Hey, Crip, why don't you just stay up there and live with the birds—the dodo birds!" Everyone laughed.

Theo exploded in fury. Letting out a fierce yell, he leaped off the branch, which was directly over Marquez, who was so shocked to see Theo jump that he forgot to move out of the way. Theo's plunging body slammed into Marquez, and the two crashed hard to the ground. "Ow, my head, my shoulder!" cried Marquez, whose face was quickly covered in blood. He burst into tears.

Theo's legs were in pain and his braces were bent. But he didn't mind. He felt good because Marquez was crying and whimpering like a baby.

Both boys were taken to Children's Hospital on Tulane Avenue. Marquez had suffered a fractured collarbone, a broken nose, and several facial cuts. Theo's legs were broken and put in casts attached to a pulley to keep them raised. The boys were recovering in a large ward with about two dozen other ill or injured children.

Theo's aunt and uncle tried to be understanding, but they were still upset with him. "God don't like ugly," Maddie told him. "See what happens when you seek revenge? You end up hurt yourself."

"Yeah, but Marquez is hurt, too," Theo argued. "I got him good."

"How do you think you've won?" Eddie said. "You're both in the hospital for a long time. Looks to me like you both lost."

Theo's smugness vanished. He felt awful inside, as low and alone as he had after his parents' funeral. "I'm a worthless cripple and I'll always be a worthless cripple," he blurted. "I'm no good to anyone." Theo turned his head away from his aunt and uncle and wept. The constant pain and itching from his leg casts only added to his misery.

About a week before Christmas, the pulley was removed from his casts so he could at least lie flat on his bed. But that did little to cheer him up. Because of the nature of his deformed legs, he had to remain in the hospital through the new year.

Every day since the incident, his aunt or uncle came to visit. But no matter how many jokes Eddie cracked or how many pralines Maddie made, Theo sank deeper into depression. Once, when he tried to get out of bed, he slipped and knocked over the plate of ginger cookies that his aunt had baked. The plate and cookies shattered on the floor, causing a few kids in the ward to snicker. "See? I can't do anything right," he moaned.

The next day, Eddie marched into the ward and tossed Theo a shirt and blanket.

"What's this for?" asked Theo.

"I'm takin' you out of the hospital for a few hours. There's someone I want you to meet."

Eddie put him in a wheelchair, wheeled him outside, and lifted him onto the wagon. A short while later, on a street lined with elegant mansions lavishly decorated for Christmas, the wagon turned into a gated entrance that led to a courtyard with a flowing fountain ringed by poinsettias. Ahead of them stood a three-story-tall brick mansion fronted by four white columns and two black iron balconies draped in garland and large gold bows.

"Where are we?" Theo asked.

"This is the home of Jacques and Simone Sudier, the couple I work for," Eddie replied. He guided the wagon to the back of the mansion, where fellow workers greeted them. Eddie put the boy in his wheelchair and took him to a large glass-enclosed room filled with potted plants and trees, tanks of exotic fish, and cages of small dazzling birds. Flitting and flying about were bigger birds and beautiful butterflies.

"What is this place?" Theo asked.

"This is Mrs. Sudier's aviary, where she keeps her prize birds," Eddie replied.

Across the room, a woman in her forties who was tending to one of the birdcages turned around and beamed when she spotted Eddie and beckoned him over. "That's Mrs. Sudier," he whispered to Theo.

A strikingly pretty woman with a peach-colored complexion and black hair swirled up in a bun, Mrs. Sudier rubbed her hands on her gingham apron. She flashed a warm smile as they approached. "So this must be the nephew you told me about," she said.

"Yes, ma'am," said Eddie. "This here is Theo Landry."

"Delighted to meet you, Theo," she said. "I'm Simone Sudier."

The shy boy lowered his head and mumbled, "Nice to meet you, ma'am."

"Let me introduce you to my feathered friends," she said. She showed him African parrots and Australian parakeets, cockatiels and cockatoos, lovebirds and songbirds.

"I want you to meet one of my most precious birds." She motioned Eddie and Theo over to a large metal cage that contained yellow, red, and green canaries, some perching on their little swings, others zipping back and forth. "See this one here in the front corner?" she said, pointing to a pale yellow canary.

To Theo, it looked like any other canary — until he saw its twisted legs and deformed feet. It fluttered up to a perch but had difficulty remaining there without flapping its wings. *Poor little bird,* Theo thought.

"I have been raising and studying canaries for years," said Mrs. Sudier. "Last summer, I watched this baby canary peck his way through the shell. I felt sorry for him because he was hatched with bent legs and clubfeet. See how his feet are turned inward?

He can't get around as well as the other birds nor swing as grace-fully as them. He can't even cling to the side of the cage. At first, I sensed there was much sadness about the way the little fellow acted."

I know how he feels, Theo told himself.

"The baby canary seemed to understand that he was differ-ent than the other birds," she continued. "They could hop and flutter around in their cages with so much ease and grace. He would stumble or lose his grip. He couldn't be like them because of his handicap."

She glanced at Theo's legs. She didn't say anything. She didn't have to. Theo understood all too well the similarities between his condition and the bird's.

Mrs. Sudier reached into the case and held out her hand. The canary flew onto her palm and wobbled when he landed. Gently, she brought her hand out of the cage and lightly stroked his head, curling her fingers around him to give him support so he could relax his wings.

"I want you to meet Troubadour," she told Theo. "There is something very special about this canary. Listen."

After a few chirps, the little fellow burst into a medley of trilling and twittering, whistling and warbling. His singing totally captured the attention of the boy, who up until now couldn't have cared less about birds. He didn't know a tiny bird — a crip-pled one at that — could sing so superbly.

"His throat seems to have a silver lining, and the notes gurgle out like the laughter of a brook," said Mrs. Sudier. "Don't you agree, Theo?"

"Yes, ma'am."

Mrs. Sudier closed her eyes, blocking out all distractions as she listened to the canary. "Notice the musical sequence of notes, not too loud or too soft," she said with reverence. "Hear how pleasing his songs are, how dynamic they sound without becoming thin on the high notes or muddy on the low ones. His tempo and tone are flawless. He's a genius in trilling and twittering."

She opened her eyes. "When I discovered the rare singing qualities of this little crippled canary, I became more attached to him than ever before, and I named him Troubadour. And you know what, Theo? The little fellow has become the particular favorite of the whole flock. Look at them."

Theo glanced at the cage of canaries and saw them on their perches, motionless and facing Troubadour. "They've stopped flying around so they can listen to him," said Theo.

"Pretty remarkable, yes?"

"Yes, ma'am."

Troubadour continued to sing for another minute before Mrs. Sudier placed him back in the cage. "As much as I have grown deeply attached to the canary, I have decided he can serve a greater good elsewhere with his gift of song. Therefore, for Christmas, I am giving him to the Children's Hospital so that sick and injured children can be inspired by his sweet songs."

"That's very nice of you, ma'am," said Theo.

"Theo, I have an important favor to ask of you. I want you to care for the bird for as long as you are in the hospital. That means feeding him, changing his water, and cleaning out his cage. It also means taking him around the wards so all the children can hear him sing. Can you do that for me, Theo?"

The request caught Theo by surprise. *This important woman wants me to care for her special bird? Nobody has ever asked me to be in charge of anything before.* For the first time in a long time, Theo felt a surge of pride. "Yes, ma'am. I can do that."

"Stupendous!" she said, clapping her hands.

When it came time to leave, Mrs. Sudier put Troubadour in a small silver cage and placed it on Theo's lap. The bird's supplies were loaded in the back of the wagon. "Take good care of him, Theo."

"I will, ma'am. Thank you."

Back at the hospital, Theo showed off the canary to the other children in his ward. As he expected, a few made fun of him and the bird. But when Troubadour began to sing, the children in the ward fell silent. Throughout the next two days, every child, doctor, nurse, and aide in the hospital had heard — and appreciated — Troubadour's talent.

On Christmas Eve, someone said to be Papa Noel's cousin (who looked surprisingly like Uncle Eddie in a fluffy white beard) showed up at the ward and passed out Maddie's freshly made cookies, cakes, and candy to all the children. "Time to sing Christmas carols!" he cried.

They started off with "Deck the Halls," and Theo only mouthed the words. But after glancing at the birdcage where Troubadour was flapping his wings, Theo decided that maybe he should join in the singing. For "Joy to the World," his voice grew stronger, and he sang with vigor.

By "Hark the Herald Angels Sing," one voice clearly stood out above all the rest: Theo's. Never before had anyone heard a child sing with such clarity, emotion, and depth. Theo amazed himself. He had no inkling he possessed such a God-given talent.

Uncle Eddie and the other children stopped in mid-song just so they could hear Theo sing solo. His voice electrified the ward with a spirited holiday melody, and the sad boy with the bad legs soon felt truly alive and happy. Kids stared at him, not out of pity or scorn like before, but out of genuine admiration. When he finished, they applauded and shouted, "Sing again, Theo!" "Yeah, do another one!"

Theo blushed from all the attention. "I . . . I don't know. "

Uncle Eddie walked over to him and said, "Try 'Silent Night.'"

Theo looked at Troubadour for encouragement and then launched into the song in a voice reaching perfect pitch and intensity. When he finished, the room exploded in an ovation. As the clapping subsided, another lovely sound filled the ward. It was the beautiful warble of a little yellow canary.

When the New Orleans Times-Democrat heard about the canary, it ran a story about him. It ended the article this way: "The little canary genius, with his clubfeet, is at the Children's Hospital, where he is swinging in his awkward way and singing to the children of the institution. Mrs. Sudier thought it would be an important lesson for the little children. He is no doubt a source of great inspiration to them. It is a pretty lesson."

The Christmas Tree Thief

Mariah Clayton decided to spare no expense in decorating her home for Christmas even though she and her husband, Dylan, had no children.

Well, that's not entirely true. The couple had four "kids" if you considered their four large, majestic dogs as children, which in a way the Claytons did.

Gypsy, Java, Angus, and Athos were dogs known as Leonbergers. Typical of the breed, each dog had a black "mask" that extended from the nose and lips to the eyes. Each sported a long, reddish-brown coat and a thick mane that reminded you of a canine version of a lion. The two females, Gypsy and Java, weighed about 120 pounds each, but Angus, the oldest and biggest, tipped the scales at 160 pounds and stood 32 inches from the ground to the shoulder. His nine-month-old son, Athos, was the baby of the group, even though he weighed as much as the females and was still growing.

The Claytons' gentle giants were loving, intelligent, and strong, and showed exceptional loyalty, patience, and playfulness. In Athos's case, perhaps a little too much playfulness.

As a puppy, he was always getting into mischief. He assumed that any item left on the floor was for him to play with. One time he swiped Dylan's Air Jordans and sneaked out the doggy door — built jumbo-size to accommodate the huge dogs — and went behind a maple tree in the large fenced-in backyard. There, he chewed the shoes beyond recognition before he was caught in the act of burying them. Then there was the time months later when he got an idea while watching Mariah bring in the groceries. As she left the kitchen to collect the rest of her groceries from the car, Athos, who had grown a lot, stood up and, with his big paws, shoved a full plastic bag off the kitchen counter. After snatching the bag in his teeth, he charged out the doggy door and took his bounty to his favorite spot behind the maple tree. Inside the bag was a large packaged ham that was meant for a dinner party that night.

But for every naughty thing he did, Athos made up for it with his sweet temperament. He had an uncanny ability to know when Mariah or Dylan was upset or feeling low. During those moments, he would give him or her a needed lick on the hand or cheek. Sometimes he would roll on his back and paw at the air to get them to laugh.

Mariah felt that Athos was outgrowing his troublemaking puppy antics, so she felt confident he wouldn't pull any stunts while she decorated the house for the holidays in 2000.

She wanted to make this a Christmas to remember, one she

had dreamed of her whole life. It would be the first time that she and Dylan would host Christmas dinner for Mariah's three siblings, their spouses, and their children since the death of her mother eight months earlier. Mariah had never cooked dinner for fifteen before, but she felt up to the task. Fortunately, the couple's rural upstate New York home featured an open kitchen and dining area big enough to accommodate everyone.

Throughout the house, Mariah displayed her late mother's Santa Claus doll collection that she had inherited. The banister and mantel were decked out in fresh garland with silver and red bows and tiny white lights. Above the mantel, she hung a large evergreen wreath. Every table and shelf had a Christmas-themed figurine made of wood or porcelain. Artwork on the walls was replaced with holiday signs such as WE BELIEVE IN SANTA and framed posters of Santa. Red silk poinsettias adorned the living room and dining room. On the coffee table stood a three-foot-tall centerpiece of a Christmas tree that she had made out of pinecones painted gold.

The dogs watched in fascination as Mariah spun her holiday magic. Sure, there were moments when one or the other would stick a head into a box of decorations or playfully swipe at a ribbon or bow, but for the most part, the Leonbergers were on their best behavior — even Athos. Okay, he did give in to temptation once when he yanked off a string of garland that was dangling from the mantel. But that happened during the early stages of decorating, and he showed appropriate remorse after Mariah said, "No, Athos!"

The house was aglow in the holiday spirit when Dylan came

home and announced to Mariah, "I have brought you the perfect Christmas tree!"

Sensing this was good news, the dogs barked and wagged their tails. Within a few minutes, Mariah and Dylan had fit a flawlessly shaped seven-foot-tall Norway spruce into the tree stand in the living room next to the fireplace.

"Oh, Dylan, it's so pretty." Mariah beamed. "We don't have to trim any branches or anything. Look how straight it is! I can't wait for us to start decorating it."

"Can it be right after dinner?" asked Dylan. "I'm starving — and apparently the dogs are, too. At least, Athos is."

Athos was sitting in the kitchen doorway, holding his bowl in his mouth.

"All right, everyone," said Mariah. "I get the hint."

After the meal, Dylan loaded up the CD player with the couple's favorite Christmas songs and started a toasty blaze in the fireplace. "It's time to trim the tree," he said.

Over the next few hours, the two of them sang carols while they turned the spruce into a holiday masterpiece. Of course, it meant stepping over and around their Leonbergers, who refused to budge from their comfortable spots in front of the fire.

The couple threaded the lights — hundreds of them — in the branches, making sure that each little bulb could be seen. Then they pulled out of cushioned boxes beautiful, delicate ornaments. With a loving touch, they hung gold, silver, and burgundy decorations shaped like balls, teardrops, and swirls. They placed hand-carved, hand-blown, and hand-sewn ornaments made of wood, glass, and fabric. They hooked on the branches expensive Lenox crystal snowflakes, trees, and stars—gifts that Dylan had given Mariah for previous Christmases.

Keeping their eyes on the couple, each dog seemed to be interested in a favorite kind of ornament. Gypsy raised her head every time a glittery tassel was fastened to a branch. Java's ears perked up whenever a tiny music box decoration was wound up and added to the tree. Angus and Athos wagged their tails as little tin bells were hung.

Mariah put up ornaments that she had saved from her childhood, including a porcelain ballet dancer and a leaping reindeer—and a faded plastic gingerbread boy that she had painted when she was nine.

Her eyes welled up when she hung some of her late mother's decorations, which had been divvied up among Mariah, her sister, and two brothers. "I sure miss Mom," she said with a sniffle.

Wanting to comfort her, Dylan climbed down from a stepladder, but Athos reached her first and licked her hand. "Oh, you're so sweet, Athos," she murmured as tears began to trickle down her cheeks. Dylan hugged her and said, "Your mother would be so happy and proud to see how you decorated this house."

The touching moment was interrupted when Athos insisted on shoving his way between the two. Then he sat up and put a paw on each of them. Clenching a big red bow between his teeth, he looked like he was wearing clown lips. The two burst out laughing.

"How does he know just the right time to make me feel better?" she asked, wiping her face.

"He's a special dog—one in a million," Dylan replied.

When all the decorations were on the tree, Dylan climbed onto the stepladder for the final touch — placing the angel on the top. He then joined Mariah as the two stepped back to admire their work.

"Looks good," said Dylan.

"'*Good*'? Why, it's absolutely picture-perfect beautiful!" Mariah gushed. "I don't know how it could look any better."

"I know how," said Dylan. He left the room and returned with a small box wrapped in green ribbon and handed it to her.

"For me?" she asked.

"Well, sort of. Go ahead and open it."

Inside were four silver ornaments — each in the shape of a Leonberger. At the bottom of each decoration was the name of one of their dogs.

"Oh, how precious!" she squealed. She kissed Dylan and then put the ornaments on the tree. "Now it is even more perfect!"

The couple sat down on the floor in front of the fire and sipped eggnog while the dogs cuddled at their feet and legs. Glancing out the window, Mariah smiled. "And to top off the night, it's snowing!"

Content and tired, the couple extinguished the fire, unplugged the lights, and headed up the festively decorated stairs. Like every night, they were followed by their Leonbergers, who had their own sleeping area on the floor by the foot of the bed.

The couple fell into a deep sleep. The next morning, Mariah woke up first. When she opened her eyes, she looked outside and saw a glistening blanket of fresh snow. *Oh, it's going to be a beautiful day*, she thought.

When she sat up in bed and gazed at her slumbering pets, she was puzzled. She rubbed her eyes and looked again. *What happened to the dogs?* She hopped out of bed, went over to them, and began to giggle. Gypsy, Java, and Angus were still snoozing — and were covered with toilet paper. *They look like mummies. There can be only one explanation for this — Athos!* The young dog was not in the room.

It took only a minute to unravel what had happened. Sometime during the night, Athos went into the bathroom and took a spare roll of toilet paper that had been sitting on the floor. Then he came back into the bedroom and somehow draped his canine buddies in TP. Being the gentle souls that they were, the trio didn't put up any fuss and simply went back to sleep.

What will Athos think of next? she chuckled to herself. After removing the "tissue nightshirts," she put on her robe, went to the window, and admired the winter landscape. But then she spotted some unusual objects on the main-floor deck. She quickly realized that scattered across the deck were gold-painted pine-cones — the very same gold-painted pinecones from her three-foot-high centerpiece.

Oh, no, not Athos again!

She hurried down the stairs and went into the living room. Sure enough, the centerpiece on the coffee table was missing. *Oooh, that dog is in big trouble.*

Mariah took two steps toward the kitchen and froze. *Something's not right.* Then it hit her like a giant snowball. *The tree is gone!*

A path of pine needles, broken ornaments, and crushed lightbulbs led from where the tree once stood through the kitchen and directly to the doggy door. *That can't be possible. There's no way.*

But once she looked outside, she knew otherwise. Athos was standing next to the once-beautiful Norway spruce that was now in the middle of the backyard. Scattered all over were smashed and chewed-up ornaments on the snow-covered deck and ground.

"Dylan! Dylan!" Mariah shouted. "Come down here right now and see what *your* dog did!"

Yawning and squinting, Dylan tromped down the stairs and went into the kitchen. "What's wrong, honey?"

"Didn't you notice anything unusual in the living room?" she asked in a miffed voice.

He shook his head and then backtracked his steps. "Hey, what happened to the Christmas tree?"

"Athos!" she hissed.

"What about him?"

"See for yourself."

He stared out the window and muttered, "I don't believe it."

"Our beautiful, picture-perfect tree. Ruined by *your* dog."

"Why is it every time Athos does something bad, he suddenly becomes *my* dog?"

Examining the scene of the crime, they figured out that Athos had knocked over the seven-foot tree. They didn't hear anything because they were both sleeping so soundly. Athos picked up the tree by the middle of the trunk and carried it across the room and into the kitchen, where he dropped it. Stepping through the doggy door, he turned around, gripped the top of the tree in his jaws, and kept yanking until it cleared the opening. Then he dragged it into the yard and proceeded to chomp, chew, and bury the ornaments.

"Look at him, Dylan. He's standing behind the tree with a happy expression on his face, as if to say, 'See how much better it looks out here?'"

By now, the other dogs had awakened and went outside to check out Athos's misdeed. Meanwhile, Dylan got dressed and joined them. From the back door, Mariah spotted several red stains in the snow. "Dylan, I think one of the dogs is bleeding!"

When he inspected the area, Dylan reported back, "I have good news and bad news. The good news is that it's not blood. The bad news is that it's from chewed-up silk poinsettias."

Mariah groaned. "My Christmas decorations . . . gone to the dogs!"

When Dylan came back inside, Mariah said, "I don't know whether to laugh or cry."

"You might as well laugh because crying won't do any good."

"But, Dylan, what about all the work I put into the decorating and all the time we spent trimming the tree? What about all the broken and irreplaceable ornaments? What about our picture-perfect Christmas tree?"

"Look at it this way, Mariah: The Christmas tree — no matter how beautiful — would have lasted only through the holidays. But the Christmas story that Athos has given us will last for generations."

The First Noel

L ulu the Manx cat loved Christmas.

What she really loved most was the Christmas tree. Every year, when Jeff and Deanna Sawyer and their daughters, Traci and Kim, put up the Yule tree, Lulu gazed in fascination from her nearby vantage point on the fireplace mantel.

The stocky gray-and-black cat, who had a nub for a tail (which is common among the breed), followed every move the foursome made as they trimmed the tree with twinkling lights and sparkling ornaments. She waited patiently until the final touches were complete — the decorations spaced evenly apart, the gap in the lower right side covered up with the larger ornaments, and the angel placed on the top. When the tree was finished to their — and her — satisfaction, Lulu made her move.

She jumped down from the mantel and sauntered over to the tree. She sniffed the pine needles and walked around the trunk, occasionally stopping to examine the decorations dangling from the lowest branches. Then, in one quick bound, she leaped into the tree and momentarily disappeared. With effortless grace, she worked her way up, barely causing the branches to move. It was as if she knew she had to be extra careful so she wouldn't jostle any of the ornaments and cause them to crash to the floor.

Once she found her spot, which usually was about two-thirds of the way up, she nestled on a thick branch and inched out just enough so that she had a wide view of the room. And there she stayed for an hour or more, her body brushing up against the tree's flashing red, blue, yellow, and green miniature lights.

The Sawyers had heard "horror stories" of crazed kittens and cats attacking trimmed Christmas trees, knocking off ornaments, ripping decorations, and toppling trees. But in all the years they had Lulu, not once did she so much as accidentally break a branch or destroy an ornament. Knowing she turned the Christmas tree into her cat tree, the Sawyers made sure that the ornaments were securely fastened. Okay, there was one time when she caused damage. It happened when she climbed to the top to sniff the angel and knocked it off. The angel fell, breaking its halo.

As for the packages under the tree, well, that was another story. Lulu simply couldn't resist biting the bows and tags off the presents. She had a thing for red bows. Not only did she rip them off the boxes but she hid them, usually under the living room couch. That was bad enough. But what really drove the family nuts was when she tore off the tags on packages that had the same kind of wrapping paper.

Because of her misbehavior, Christmas morning always featured at least one bit of confusion over who was giving what to whom. The typical conversation went something like this:

"Whose gift is this? It doesn't have a tag on it."

"I think it's mine."

"Yours to give or yours to receive?"

"Oooh, that Lulu!"

Knowing that efforts to stop her from tearing off the tags were futile, the Sawyers accepted it as one of Lulu's quirks and made it part of the family's holiday tradition.

On Christmas morning, Lulu no longer watched quietly from somewhere in the middle of the tree. Instead, she insisted on being in the center of the action. As presents were opened, she dived under the wrapping paper, rolled around in ribbons, and, of course, ran off with the red bows.

For fourteen years, Lulu had played the starring role during Christmastime at the Sawyer household. So it was perfectly understandable why the entire family was in a funk when the 2003 holiday season arrived. Lulu was gone. She had vanished without a trace.

The Sawyers lived far from town on a ranch in Montana's Bitterroot Valley, where they raised horses. They also had several goats and donkeys, and a chicken coop.

Although Lulu was a house cat, she occasionally went outside on sunny days, never wandering too far from the house. She learned early in life that the ranch could be a dangerous place when a billy goat gored her while she tried stealing his food. After she recovered from her wound, she had no desire to explore the rest of the ranch.

In September 2003, construction began on an addition to the Sawyers' home. For weeks, the banging of hammers, whining of saws, and whirring of drills filled the air. The commotion and dust eventually became too much for the aging cat. Lulu tried hiding under beds and then in closets. But the places failed to offer her the comfort and security she wanted.

So on an exceptionally noisy October afternoon, Lulu scurried out an open door and disappeared. The Sawyers, who didn't notice she was gone until dusk, searched the grounds and the stables without success. The next morning, the family asked the workers if they had seen her walking off the previous day. None of them had, although one worker said he saw her lurking by his truck shortly before quitting time.

Traci, twelve, and Kim, eleven, rode their horses from one end of the ranch to the other without finding any trace of Lulu. They called nearby ranchers, asking them to look out for the missing cat, who wasn't wearing a collar with any identification tags.

After a week without any sighting of Lulu, Jeff told Deanna and the girls, "I think we have to face the cold hard truth that Lulu is dead."

"He's right, girls," said Deanna. "With temperatures in the twenties at night, she couldn't possibly survive. I'm guessing a coyote got her."

"I feel so bad," said Traci.

"I really, really miss her," said Kim.

"We all do," said Deanna. "But she had a good life. Fourteen years. She came into my life before either one of you was born. She was there watching over you when you were each in your crib. She was devoted to you, to all of us."

A couple months later, when the holiday season arrived, the family put up the Christmas tree and decorated the house. And although they seemed happy, they each felt a twinge of sadness because Lulu wasn't there.

"Christmas just isn't the same without Lulu," Kim complained.

"I know," said Traci. "I keep expecting to see her sticking her head out from the branches."

"And the bows," Deanna added. "I keep thinking I'll find red bows under the couch."

For the first time since Lulu was adopted, the Sawyers had no problem identifying their presents on Christmas morning.

Time eventually eased any lingering pangs of sadness over Lulu's disappearance. In fact, her name never came up until the following Christmas when the family began decorating the house and putting up the Yule tree. Every time one of the girls wrote a name on a tag or taped a bow on a package, they were reminded of their beloved cat.

Two years later, during the 2005 Christmas season, Deanna and Jeff were strolling downtown, admiring the holiday window displays. Although the couple often came into town, which was fifteen miles from their ranch, they seldom spent any time shopping other than for necessities, so visiting the clothing stores and antique shops downtown was a treat.

As they passed the Black Oak Dry Goods Store, Jeff suggested, "Let's go inside and look around. Maybe we'll find something for the girls."

The store was buzzing with holiday shoppers. Deanna was flicking through a sales rack when she heard several distinctive meows. "Did you hear that, Jeff?" she asked. "It sounded just like Lulu."

"They probably have a store cat," he said. They looked around but couldn't locate where the meowing was coming from.

Deanna stopped a clerk and asked, "Do you keep a cat in the store?"

"Yes, we do."

"Where is she?"

Pointing to the top of a shelf in the front window, the clerk said, "Right behind you."

Deanna wheeled around and looked up. She clutched Jeff's arm and said, "Oh . . . my . . . God! Jeff, doesn't she look exactly like Lulu?"

"The same face, the same color," he replied. "You don't suppose . . ."

Staring directly into the cat's eyes, Deanna said, "Lulu? Is that you?"

The cat meowed and worked her way down off the shelf. When she reached the counter in front of Jeff and Deanna, she pranced back and forth, mewing and purring. Deanna leaned in, and the cat licked her face and gently bit her nose.

"Lulu! It *is* you! You're not dead after all!" Deanna picked up the cat and held her tight.

"Don't get your hopes up, Deanna," warned Jeff. "There are a lot of Manx cats who look alike."

The owner of the store, Jane Goldman, walked over to the couple and said, "You must have a way with animals. Usually, she's shy around strangers and likes to watch people from the store window or from the top of the shelf."

"We had a cat who looks identical to her, but she disappeared a little over two years ago," Deanna told Mrs. Goldman. "How long have you had her?"

"It's been almost exactly two years," the store owner replied. "I first saw her sometime in the fall of 2003 in the alley behind the store. I assumed she was a stray or an abandoned cat because she had no collar. She was sad-looking and dirty. Very skittish and hungry. She wouldn't let me get too close to her. I'm an animal lover. I have three dogs, two cats, and two fish at home. I couldn't let her starve, so every day I put out a little bowl of milk and some food by the alley door. She ate everything and soon I gained her trust. When winter set in, she decided to check us out and came into the store. She hasn't left since. She became our first mascot. Because it was the holidays, we named her Noel."

Mrs. Goldman took the cat from Deanna and petted her. "The front window is her favorite place to sit and watch the world go by. Everybody in town knows her. Whenever my regular customers come in and don't see her in the window, they ask if she's all right."

"Mrs. Goldman, I'm absolutely convinced that your Noel is my Lulu," said Deanna. "Lulu has a scar on her stomach from when she was attacked by a billy goat." Reaching for the cat, she said, "May I?" Taking the cat from the woman's arms, Deanna cradled her so her tummy was showing. Deanna brushed the cat's hair with her fingers to reveal a three-inch scar. "See? It *is* Lulu."

Disappointed by the news, Mrs. Goldman asked, "How did she end up *here*?"

"We were remodeling our house two years ago in the fall, and Lulu couldn't stand all the commotion. She left the house and disappeared," Deanna explained. "We live fifteen miles away from town, so we're not sure how she showed up in the back of your store."

"I suspect that when she got out of the house, she hid in the back of one of the worker's trucks, and no one knew it," said Jeff. "He probably drove into town, and she jumped out and ended up in the alley."

A look of resignation crept across Mrs. Goldman's face. She reached out and stroked Lulu's head. "She's such a sweet cat."

"Mrs. Goldman, you've been so kind and loving to Lulu," Deanna said. "You took her in when no one else would. I know you're attached to her. But we have two girls at home who have known this cat their whole lives . . . and they miss her. Please, will you let us take her back to her real home?"

Mrs. Goldman continued to pet the cat, not taking her eyes off her. Finally, the woman looked at the couple and said, "I have fourteen grandchildren, so I understand how deeply attached kids can get to their pets. I'm so very fond of Noel . . . I mean, Lulu . . . but I can't deny Lulu her rightful home. This was meant to be."

Deanna threw her arms around the woman and gushed, "Oh, thank you so much. My children are going to cry from joy."

"I'm going to miss her," said Mrs. Goldman. "She made a wonderful shop cat."

On the way from town, Deanna used her cell phone to call the girls. When they were both on the line, she told them, "Dad and I have a surprise for you two, so don't leave the house."

"What is it, Mom?" asked Traci.

"You'll have to wait and see. All I can say is this surprise is just *purr*-fect."

When the couple arrived, the girls flew out of the house, shouting, "What's our surprise?"

"Who do you miss most at this time of year?" Deanna asked them.

"Lulu, of course," Kim answered. "But she's . . ."

"Alive!" shrieked Traci, seeing the Manx cat peeking out from under Jeff's jacket. "You found Lulu!" The girls ran over to Jeff, grabbed the cat, and showered her in kisses and hugs.

As they took turns petting her, Kim said, "If this is all we get for Christmas, it's the best Christmas ever!"

But that's not the end of the story.

Two days after Christmas, Mrs. Goldman received a call from a woman who lived across the street from the store. "Did you lose your mascot?" the neighbor asked.

"Well, yes I did. But not in the way you might think. Why do you ask?"

"Because I found a black-and-gray cat with a bobbed tail. I think it's your mascot."

At first, Mrs. Goldman wondered if Lulu had somehow run off again and made her way back to town. But when she went over to the neighbor's, she knew instantly that it was a different cat. This one was a Manx cat with similar markings, but much darker and younger than Lulu.

After explaining what had happened to her shop cat, Mrs. Goldman told the neighbor, "I'll take this stray and make her my newest mascot."

"What a Christmas present it is for this cat."

"Yes, and in keeping with the holiday, I'm going to name her Noel Too."

Backwoods Blessing

Playing his fiddle, Nathan Fairfield led his fellow loggers in singing lively Christmas carols by a roaring fire in the camp lodge. He didn't hear the knocking on the door until they had finished belting out "Jingle Bells."

Certainly no one expected to have a visitor at this time of year in the deep woods of northern Maine, especially at night in a howling snowstorm. "'Tain't likely that even a fool would be out at night in this wicked blizzard," Nathan told his men.

"Maybe old Saint Nick came to give you a lump of coal," cracked one of the lumbermen.

With some uneasiness, Nathan opened the door. Facing him was a hulking, bearded man in a snow-covered hooded fur coat and matching fur-lined boots that were strapped onto snowshoes. Over his shoulder was a string of beaver pelts.

I wonder if he's the hunter and trapper who never stops to talk to us, Nathan thought. "Come in," said Nathan, motioning quickly to the young man as wind-whipped snow swirled through the open door. "'Tain't a fit night for man nor beast."

The visitor stepped inside and threw back his hood, revealing curly brown hair the same color as his thick beard, which was mostly caked in ice. His sad blue eyes darted around the room, taking in brief glimpses of each of the fourteen loggers, the fireplace, the table with plates and platters from a just-finished meal, and the boughs of evergreen decorating the walls. He cleared his throat and mumbled, "Didn't mean to interrupt."

"No interruption at all, my friend," Nathan said. "Come join us for some holiday cheer. It is, after all, Christmas Eve."

"It is?" he said with a blink.

I'm pretty sure he's the shy trapper, Nathan thought. "I'm Nathan Fairfield, foreman at this camp." Pointing to the loggers, he said, "And this is my crew."

The men held up their drinks, raised their fingers, or nodded to acknowledge the stranger. He shifted his feet, feeling awkward and not knowing how best to respond. He finally nodded back, but without saying anything.

He didn't even offer his name. Must be that trapper. Staying in the holiday spirit, Nathan asked him, "How about a drink to warm you up? Or maybe vittles to fill your belly?"

The man shook his head. "I'm lookin' to trade my pelts for flour, sugar, and coffee. I'm plum out."

"Sure we can work a trade. But, please, come share our Christmas feast, Mister . . . Mister . . . ?"

"Bruce. Dick Bruce."

Nathan glanced at the other men, who now trained their eyes squarely on the visitor. *So it's really him in the flesh!* They had heard stories about the reclusive and infamous Trapper Dick.

Dick Bruce was a natural-born loner who came from an extremely poor family. He left home when he was only thirteen — some say he ran away from a cruel father — and learned to trap, hunt, and fish on his own. Turning into a strong, resourceful young man, he ran backcountry traplines that extended throughout the Aroostook watershed.

Trapper Dick moved into a rickety abandoned one-room log cabin and chinked the cracks between the logs with moss and repaired the cedar shakes on the roof. He made his own furniture out of branches and logs and cooked over an open fire outside.

Near where he kept his various traplines, he set up primitive campsites made mostly of woven evergreen branches about three feet wide and six feet long — just enough to give him shelter. He hunted, fished, and trapped in all seasons, even in subzero weather, and soon developed a reputation as one of the region's best trappers.

Refusing to step foot in any town, Trapper Dick dealt with only a few select people who traded goods with him for his skins. If he spotted a lumberjack or hunter in the woods, he deliberately hurried off the trail to avoid talking to them.

A path that led to one of his traplines crossed a dirt road near Nathan's lumber camp. Several times over the previous two years, the foreman and other loggers had seen Dick in the woods and called out to him, but the trapper never responded. So it was easy to understand why on this Christmas Eve in 1903, the lumber-jacks were surprised that Trapper Dick was visiting their lodge.

It took some coaxing from Nathan before the trapper agreed to eat their leftovers. When the loggers began singing again, he pushed his plate aside and listened with intense interest.

"Join us in a Christmas carol," urged Nathan.

His eyes downcast, Trapper Dick said, "Don't know any. Never heard one before."

"Surely you sang carols at school or at church."

The trapper shook his head. "Never went to school or church. Singin' wasn't allowed at home."

"Then how did you celebrate Christmas?"

He shrugged and mumbled, "Never did."

"Have you ever heard this one?" Nathan picked up his fiddle and began playing and singing the first few lines of "Deck the Halls."

When Nathan stopped, Trapper Dick said, "Nope. Mind if we trade now?"

After they reached a quick agreement, Nathan said, "Tell me something, Dick. We see you walk by the camp several times a year, yet you never stop. Why don't you ever socialize with me and my men?"

The trapper was lost in thought for a moment, wondering how much to reveal. Whether it was Nathan's gentle manner or the warmth he felt in the room, Dick decided to open up. "Truth is, if I stop and get to know people, I'll just feel lonesome when we part."

"You won't feel so lonely if you visit us more often."

"Better if I don't, 'cause my survival depends on it. If I keep my distance from people, I can't catch their cold or flu. I have to stay healthy and fit or I'll die out there."

"Well, we're not sick," said Nathan. "At least spend the night here and enjoy the holiday cheer. You must be going nuts talking to no one but the beavers."

"I should go."

"Go? Out in this winter storm? Are you crazy?"

"I'll be fine." Dick loaded up his pack and headed for the door.

"Wait," said Nathan. "I'll be right back." He went into another room and returned holding a squirming black male puppy. "Merry Christmas!"

Trapper Dick looked dumbfounded. "What do you mean?"

"We found him about a week ago in the woods. We don't know what happened to the mother. Cute little guy, isn't he? I think he's a black Labrador mix. He's for you."

"Me? What am I gonna do with a dog? It's hard enough to care for myself."

The puppy yipped and wagged his tail as Nathan held him up toward Dick. Suddenly the dog slipped free and began to fall. The trapper instinctively reached out and caught the puppy before he hit the floor. As Dick brought the puppy closer to him, the dog leaned forward and licked the trapper's rough beard.

"He's taken a shine to you," said Nathan. "In no time, you'll take a shine to him, too. He'll keep you company."

For several silent seconds, the trapper stared at the dog he was holding before thrusting him toward Nathan. "I don't think so."

Nathan held up his hands and said with a smile, "It's rude to turn down a Christmas present."

Dick held the dog closer to him and began to weaken. "I never got a real Christmas present before — at least, none I can remember." By now, the puppy was snuggling under the trapper's beard. A slight grin creased across Dick's face. "Well, I guess I could train him."

He tucked the pooch under his coat and headed for the door. "Much obliged."

"Merry Christmas!" said Nathan and the loggers.

"Same to you," he replied.

Over the next year, the lumberjacks spotted Trapper Dick twice. Both times, they hailed him from a distance. Although he declined to go over to them, he did give them a halfhearted wave. A black Labrador mix was seen by his side.

On a sunny but frigid afternoon shortly before Christmas 1904, there was a knock on the door of the logging camp lodge. "Come on in!" Nathan shouted. When the door opened, Nathan turned around and bellowed, "Well, I'll be! It's Trapper Dick! And who's that critter with you?"

"Pete, the dog you gave me. He's grown up. Smart as a whip." The trapper smiled big enough to reveal glistening white teeth. There was a sparkle in his eyes that had been missing in his previous visit.

"So what brings you here, Trapper Dick?"

"I, uh, wanted to wish you a Merry Christmas." He reached into his backpack and pulled out a split two-foot-long log. On the flat side of the log was carved the heads of a dog and of an owl. "Here, this is for you."

Nathan held it up and examined the intricate work. The dog was a spitting image of Pete. The owl was definitely a barn owl. "It's beautiful, Dick. The detail is extraordinary. Did you carve this?"

"Yep."

"Thank you very much."

Dick beamed. "Glad you like it."

Nathan couldn't help but notice that the trapper had such a different manner about him. He was less shy and more cheerful. "I assume the dog in the carving is Pete," said Nathan. "And the owl?"

"I can explain. Mind if we sit down?"

Nathan motioned toward the table. When they sat down, the trapper said, "I have something to tell—and 'tain't no tall tale." With Pete at his side, Dick stroked the dog's head and began, "I was deeply touched when you gave me the pup. I never had been given a present before. When I got him home, I named him Pete after my baby brother who died in a flu epidemic. The dog was easy to train and follows me everywhere. He alerts me to any danger, such as bears or wolves.

"Believe it or not, a few months ago Pete made friends with a wild barn owl. At night, the bird would land next to him and hop around. Pete would leap at it in a playful way, but he made sure never to catch it or harm it.

"I thought about shootin' the owl because of the racket it made at night. But when I realized how much Pete enjoyed the bird's company, I just couldn't bring myself to kill it. The old varmint continued to hoot away. I got used to it after a fashion and concluded to let the pair have their fun.

"They had a habit of gettin' together on moonlit nights and raisin' a fearful racket. The owl would perch on a stump and hoot, and Pete would sit at the base and howl. The more she hooted, the more he howled, and it would rile me until I got to thinkin' of how strange and funny it all was and began to laugh.

"I'd see them every now and then fussin' around in the woods, but the moment the old owl laid eyes on me, she would fly out of sight so fast that there was no gettin' a bead on her if I wanted to.

"Those two grew real close as time went on. Soon a strange thing happened. Pete began to disappear after meals. I discovered he'd eat what he wanted and carry the remainder to a spot in the forest where he left it for the owl to eat when the coast was clear.

"But then the owl disappeared, or at least I never saw or heard her for several nights. I didn't think much of it until the pup got to stayin' away pretty much all night. He'd sneak off when he thought I was asleep, and a couple of times he didn't come back till daylight, which wasn't like him at all. One mornin', he didn't get in till noon, so I thought I'd investigate.

"The next night, after a light snow had fallen, I watched Pete. After I pretended to be asleep, he dug up a piece of venison he had hidden earlier that day and off he trotted. I waited fifteen minutes and followed. It was easy trackin' his trail in the moon-light. After I'd gone 'bout two miles, I heard a sort of low, hootin' cry and then whines. I crept forward carefully, and there, in a little open space, close to Silver Brook, was Pete lyin' with his nose between his paws, watchin' the owl eat the venison.

"I didn't quite catch the meanin' of it at first, but I soon saw that the owl had been caught in a mink trap I had set the year before and forgotten about. That dog had been feedin' the owl ever since her foot got snagged.

"I went over to the owl and unsprung the trap. Pete cried like a baby, and the owl was scared to death of me. But when they found I meant the owl no harm, they quieted down. Since then, the owl has been quite friendly toward me. Her leg is damaged and she'll always be lame."

Trapper Dick looked straight into Nathan's eyes and continued, "Seein' how well the dog and owl got along, it got me to thinkin'. I've been huntin' and trappin' in the wild for 'bout a dozen years and I haven't spoken to but a half dozen people in all that time. I should make friends, just like i did with Pete, and Pete with that owl. It won't hurt me none to be friendlier when I meet other humans. Once I made up my mind to do just that, I thought, why not start with you, 'cause you're the first person to give me a Christmas present."

"That's mighty nice of you, Dick. Mighty nice." Nathan remained quiet for a while as he stared at the carving. He let out a sigh and said, "I'll let you in on a little secret. I don't have any family. I've been on my own for a long time and, being a foreman in a lumber camp, well, I don't get any gifts. You're the first person to give me a Christmas present since I was a kid."

The Christmas Goose

"**S**top it!" Trent Mason ordered his grandsons Chase and Dane. "I will not tolerate any more fighting in my house! Didn't you boys learn anything today?"

"Sorry, Pops," said Chase, thirteen. Pointing to his eleven-year-old brother, Dane, he said, "But he started it."

"I did not," Dane protested. "You stole my Game Boy."

"Well, you had it coming. You took the batteries out of *my* Game Boy."

"Enough!" Trent thundered. "Now give me the Game Boys."

With some reluctance, the brothers handed them over. It had been a bad day for them. They had been bickering and annoying each other ever since they arrived at their grandparents' sprawling home in rural Wisconsin two days earlier for the annual Christmas family gathering. Still, they had managed to stay out of trouble because they had four cousins to play with. Unfortunately for the brothers, on this morning — the day before

Christmas — Dane deliberately shoved Chase off the top bunk bed over some silly insult, so in retaliation Chase tripped Dane halfway down the stairs. Neither one was hurt, thank goodness. But their rotten behavior resulted in their being grounded for the day. They had to stay with their grandfather while their cousins, parents, aunts, uncles, and grandmother went on an old-fashioned, horse-drawn sleigh ride.

Trent, who was on crutches from a recent skiing accident, softened his tone, but made it clear he was disappointed in the boys. "If ever there is a time to reflect on the need for peace and harmony, it's at Christmastime," he said. "Why don't you think about that outside."

The brothers groaned. "But it's *cold* out there," Dane complained.

Trent frowned and said, "It's winter. It's Wisconsin. Of course it's cold. But the sun is out and the snow is packed. Get yourselves bundled up and ski around the property. Maybe you'll work off some of that aggressive energy. And stay away from the pond, because the ice isn't thick enough to support your weight. I'm going to take a nap, so don't bother me."

Chase and Dane donned their ski outfits, slipped into their cross-country skis, and gripped their poles. They left the house and began their trek on their grandparents' thirty snow-blanketed acres. The property, which was surrounded by farms, had a creek-fed four-acre body of water called Pops's Pond on the north end next to a dense wooded area.

A strong Canadian cold front had blown through the region three days earlier, sending temperatures plunging below zero. But on this day, the sun had warmed the afternoon to the mid-twenties, and the wind was calm.

As the boys trudged on their skis, they couldn't help but stop and fling snowballs at each other. At one point, Chase skied ahead and hid in a thicket of pines. When Dane came by, Chase pulled back a snow-covered branch and let go. It sprang forward, launching a swatch of snow that smacked into Dane's face. "Gotcha good!" Chase laughed before skiing away.

Dane got out of his skis and, taking a shortcut through the pines, raced ahead while plotting his revenge. As Chase approached, Dane charged out from behind a tree and leveled his brother with a tackle that would have impressed the Green Bay Packers.

Kicking off his skis, Chase fought back and got on top of Dane. Just as he was smashing snow in his younger brother's face, an eerie noise echoed off the hills. It sounded like a cross between the cry of a baby and the honk of a horn. Both boys stopped fighting. "What was that?" asked Chase.

Dane shrugged. They heard it again. "It's coming from Pops's Pond."

They got up, dusted the snow off themselves, and hurried down to the iced-over pond. Out in the middle, about fifty yards away from them, a large white farm goose was flapping its left wing. Crowding around it were four wild black Canada geese.

Every once in a while, one of the geese would go up to the white goose and peck at it. Dane picked up some snow, packed it into a hard ball, and threw it toward the wild geese. It landed harmlessly nearby. Then Chase fired one, which landed closer. "I bet I can hit one of them before you can," he said.

They fired several more. Only a couple of snowballs exploded close enough to the geese to spray them with snow. The wild geese squawked and skittered to the opposite end of the pond.

"Let's try for the white goose," said Dane, preparing to hurl another snowball. Chase grabbed his brother's arm and stopped him. "What did you do that for?" asked Dane.

"The goose hasn't moved. I think he's stuck in the ice."

"How could that happen?"

"He probably fell asleep in the pond, and when the weather turned really cold, the water froze around him," Chase said. "See? He's not going anywhere even though he's flapping his wing. And that sound he's making? It's a distress call. He's stuck, and if he doesn't get free, he'll die from hunger or cold. Or some animal will go out on the ice and kill him."

"I wish we could save him," said Dane.

"Let's try."

"How, Chase? Pops said not to go on the ice because it's too dangerous."

Paying no heed to the warning, Chase cautiously stepped onto the ice. "It's thick enough." He took another two steps. *Crack! Crack!* The ice gave way, and he fell into the frigid water up to his shins. Dane burst out laughing.

"Help me out!" Chase screamed, holding out his arm.

Dane gripped Chase's hand and began to pull, but unexpectedly Chase yanked back. Because he was heavier and a little stronger, Chase threw his brother off balance. Dane pitched forward onto the thin ice, which collapsed under him so that his feet and legs plunged into the freezing water. "You jerk! Why'd you do that?" Dane yelled.

"Because you laughed at me."

Grumbling at each other, they scrambled out of the bone-numbing pond and hustled over to the lake house—a one-room cabin used by family members as a bathhouse during the summer when they swam, and a warm-up shelter in the winter when they skated. The boys brought a kerosene heater out onto the porch and lit it to dry out.

Then they watched in silence as the four wild geese returned to the goose and began pecking away. "Are they trying to kill him?" asked Dane.

"I think so . . . no . . . wait." Chase stood up for a better look. "Wow, that's pretty amazing!"

"What is?"

"Dane, they're not trying to harm the goose. They're trying to *save* him. They're pecking away at the ice so they can free him."

The geese's long necks lifted and then curved down as they worked on the ice. All the while, the white goose remained still and quiet.

"That's really cool," said Dane.

Boom! Boom! Boom! Several deafening bangs shattered the snowy peacefulness. "Those hunters are back," Chase growled.

"I thought Pops threw them off his property."

"He did, but they must have gotten permission to hunt on Old Man Hester's land."

Oscar Hester was a farmer whose property butted up against

the north boundary of their grandparents' land where the woods were the thickest. *Boom! Boom!*

The gunshots scared the wild geese. They flew off out of sight, protesting with angry honks and leaving the trapped goose behind.

"Are they shooting at the geese?" asked Dane.

"No, they're probably hunting quail."

Once the boys dried out and warmed up, they turned off the heater and closed up the cabin. As Chase stared out at the pond, Dane couldn't help himself. He broke off an icicle and slipped it down his brother's back.

"Dane, you jerk!" Chase pulled his shirt out from his waist, allowing the icicle to slip out and crash into pieces on the porch. Then he ran after his brother, tackled him, and shoved snow down Dane's pants. "Now we're even."

"Truce!" yelped Dane.

Chase got up. "Truce," he said, crossing his fingers behind him.

The boys were putting on their skis for the trek back to the house when they heard the goose honking and crying out. "We can't leave him out there alone," said Chase. "He'll die for sure."

"Let's get Pops."

Chase shook his head. "He's taking a nap and he made us promise not to bother him. Besides, he told us to stay away from the pond. We can do this by ourselves."

They dragged a flat-bottomed johnboat from behind the cabin and placed it on the ice. Then they tossed in a paddle and blanket from the cabin along with their ski poles. They hopped in the boat, their weight causing the ice to snap and crack. Using their poles as picks, they broke the ice in front of them and then paddled forward.

When the ice was too thick to break, Chase climbed out and began pushing the boat from the stern with Dane in the bow. "Be careful," cautioned Dane, the first decent thing he had said to his brother all day.

The boys worked their way closer to the goose, which was looking weaker. It laid its head on the ice and no longer flapped its left wing.

"I think he's dying," said Dane. Just then the ice in front of the boat broke open. "Hurry up, Chase! Get in!"

Chase tried to jump in, but his feet slipped out from under him, and he fell on his stomach on the crackling ice. It hadn't given way yet. He didn't stand up, knowing that if his weight were too concentrated on one spot, the ice would collapse under him. He remained spread-eagled.

Dane scrambled to the stern and held out the paddle. "Grab this." Chase clutched the wide part of the paddle as Dane pulled him to the side of the boat and then helped his brother get back in.

"Thanks," said Chase. "This rescue business is getting harder than I thought."

Eventually, they inched their way so the boat was next to the hapless bird, which was now starting to panic at the sight of the two humans. It raised its head, flapped its wing, and sounded its sad distress call.

"We better work quickly before he dies from a heart attack," said Dane. Leaning over the side, the boys used their ski poles to chip away at the ice until the goose was freed. But its feet were still bound in an icy chunk.

The brothers stretched out, grabbed the goose, and pulled it into the boat. "Man, this is one big goose!" said Dane. He threw the blanket around it, leaving only its head exposed.

"He looks scared," said Chase. "Talk to him, comfort him."

Dane petted the goose and calmed it down. "It's all right, Goosey. You're going to be fine. We're going to help you."

When they returned to shore, they brought the goose into the cabin and turned on the kerosene heater to melt the rest of the ice off the bird. It favored its right leg and couldn't move its right wing. The goose had settled down and didn't put up any kind of struggle. It never tried to peck or bite the boys. "I think Goosey knows we're trying to help him," said Dane.

They took turns carrying the goose back to the house. When they arrived, the boys put it in their grandfather's workshop in the basement. Then they woke him up.

Grumbling over his interrupted dream, Trent said, "I was about to go off the one-hundred-twenty-meter ski jump. You two better have a good reason for shaking me out of my dream. And it better not be because you were fighting."

"No, Pops," said Chase. "We just saved a goose from dying. He was stuck in the ice at the pond."

"What? You went out on the ice after I told you not to?"

"But we couldn't let him die," Dane explained. "We used the johnboat."

"Where is the goose?"

"In your basement."

"What?" Trent grunted. "You kids are going to be the death of me yet."

Hobbling on his crutches, Trent followed the boys to the workshop, where the goose was curled up on the blanket. "Well, I'll be darned," he said. "I *know* this goose. He belongs to Oscar Hester. This is a domesticated goose, so he can't fly. I don't know much else about him except he's awfully smart."

"What do you mean, Pops?" Dane asked.

"This is the third straight December that this goose has escaped from Hester's farm and ended up in my pond. He joins the wild geese and stays until early January, then he waddles back to the farm."

"Why?" Chase asked.

"My guess is he knows to make a hasty getaway at this time of year to avoid being served up as Hester's Christmas dinner."

Trent examined the bird. "His right leg and right wing are broken from birdshot. Probably from one of those idiot hunters I ran off the other day."

In a phone call to the animal clinic, Trent learned the veterinarian was out of town and wouldn't be back until after Christmas. So Trent put an antibiotic ointment on the injuries. "We'll take him to the vet in a couple of days."

"Are you going to call Old Man Hester?" asked Chase.

"Sure," said Trent. "*After* the holidays."

The boys grinned, knowing their grandfather was on their side. They fed the goose chopped-up vegetables straight from their hand. Each time the goose ate something, it looked right into their eyes. To the boys, its message was unmistakable: "Thank you." They petted it and talked to it and kept the rest of the family members, upon their return, from getting too close to it.

Shortly before dinner, Trent answered the phone. Covering the mouthpiece, he whispered to the boys, "It's Hester." Speaking directly into the phone, Trent said, "Merry Christmas, Oscar. What can I do for you? . . . Your goose? Did he escape again? . . . Hmm. Well, two of my grandsons just returned from the pond. Let me ask them." Turning to the boys and speaking loud enough so Hester could hear, Trent asked, "Boys, is there a goose at the pond?" They shook their head. "No, Oscar," Trent said. "There's no goose at my pond. Well, I'm sure you and Millie will still have a delicious Christmas dinner. Good-bye. Happy holidays."

The boys gave their grandfather a high five.

That night at the dinner table, Chase and Dane were given a toast for the rescue mission. Raising his glass to the boys, Trent said, "I'm not sure what has pleased me most — the fact that you two rescued a goose or that you worked together for a good cause without harming each other."

After they ate, the boys returned to the basement several times to check on the goose. It seemed to be resting comfortably, but then the bird took a turn for the worse. Worried about its recovery, Chase and Dane brought their sleeping bags to the workshop to spend the night with the goose. The boys took turns watching it, soothing it, and encouraging it. Eventually, they fell asleep. About six in the morning, they woke up and checked on the goose.

It lifted its head and gazed directly at them with the same look of gratitude as it had hours earlier. Then it laid its head back down, closed its eyes, and took its last breath. Stunned, neither boy moved for several seconds. Then they leaned their backs against each other and cried.

They went upstairs where the rest of the family had nestled around the Christmas tree, poised to dig in to their presents. Trying hard to hide their tears, the boys broke the news about the goose's death, which certainly dampened the family's holiday mood.

"I wanted to save Goosey," said Chase, his voice cracking. "I wanted to see him get better."

Dane pouted, "This has turned into the worst Christmas Day ever."

"Quite the contrary," declared Trent from his easy chair. Seeing the somber faces on each of the family members, he spread out his arms and in a cheery voice said, "Although I feel sorry for the goose, he gave all of us an extraordinary Christmas gift."

"What?" said Dane. "Sadness?"

"No. He gave you two boys a marvelous opportunity to bring out the compassion and concern for all creation that lies within you. Despite facing a big risk, you jumped at the chance to save the goose. Not many people care enough about wildlife to go as far as you two did to help an animal in trouble, even though we humans are connected to all animals in the great web of life.

"The goose would have died out there on the ice if you hadn't rescued him. At least the bird's last few hours were passed in comfort, knowing that you cared for him and tried to ease his suffering. By that selfless action, you reminded the rest of us what it means to love the world and all its living things. When you stop and think about it, isn't that one of the true meanings of Christmas?"

The Holiday Ringer

Tony Davidson knew exactly what he wanted to get his wife, Becky, and their kids for Christmas — a bloodhound puppy.

Several months earlier, Becky's eighty-five-year-old grandfather, Charles, to whom she was very close, had died. Before he retired as a sheriff's deputy in eastern Tennessee, Charles was one of the region's best-known handlers of bloodhounds. He and his dogs had tracked down lost children, wayward hikers, and escaped prisoners. At most every search-and-rescue operation in the area, Charles arrived with his super-sniffing dogs in the back of his mud-splattered pickup. Plastered on the vehicle's bumper was a sticker that said "SUPPORT YOUR LOCAL BLOODHOUND — GET LOST!" The last of his bloodhounds died of old age about a year before Charles did.

Having been raised around bloodhounds, Becky looked forward to the day when she could have her own. But with marriage and raising two young children in a small house in town, it wasn't practical to get one of those slobbery beasts for a pet. However, the family had recently moved to a bigger home with a large fenced-in yard in the countryside north of Knoxville.

To Tony, a puppy was the perfect symbol of the Christmas spirit. A puppy represented sweet innocence, exuberant energy, and unconditional love — things many people wish they had. He pictured Christmas morning: A little floppy-eared tan-and-black bloodhound peers out from under the lid of a colorful gift box, its eyes filled with awe. The pup trips over its big ears and stumbles into mounds of holiday wrapping to squeals of delight from the kids who rush to hug it. Meanwhile, Becky is overcome with happiness and can barely speak. Ah, yes, the perfect Christmas present.

About a week before the big day, Tony visited Sandra Corliss, a breeder of purebred bloodhounds. She took him to see a litter of eight-week-olds that were tugging and nipping at one another's ears and tails. His eyes fell on a male pup that scooted away from the frolic and waddled over to him. Its long, droopy ears brushed against its stubby front legs as it sat on its rump and looked up. "It's as if the puppy is saying, 'Take me! Take me!'" Tony said. "I'll buy him."

"Good choice," said Sandra. "When do you want to take him home?"

"Christmas Eve. It's a surprise for my wife and kids. They'll absolutely freak out with joy when they see him."

Sandra shook her head and declared, "You can't have him then."

Tony was surprised by her sudden change of mind. "Why not?"

"I won't let any of my pups go until after the holidays."

"I thought the best time to send a puppy to a new family is when it's about two or three months old."

"That's true, but no self-respecting breeder will let a puppy go to its new home on Christmas or during Hanukkah. It's such a hectic time with loud noises, flashing camera lights, screeching children, ringing phones, family visits, and holiday hubbub. It's traumatic enough for a pup to leave its mother and littermates. So you can imagine how stressful and frightening it could be for a puppy to suddenly be thrust into all this excitement and craziness in new surroundings. The experience can leave a lasting negative effect on the puppy's personality when it grows into an adult."

"I never thought of that," said Tony.

"The puppy should be introduced to its new home and family during a relaxed, quiet, gentle time. The holidays are absolutely the worst time to get a new puppy."

"But I had my heart set on giving my family a bloodhound for Christmas."

"And you will—but not in the way you might think."

On the days leading up to Christmas, the Davidson children—Jillian, six, and Austin, five—were itching to open their presents early. In fact, Becky found Austin peeling off the ribbon of a gaily decorated box that had his name on it. "Austin!" she scolded. "That's for you to open on Christmas morning."

"But, Mommy, I can't wait that long. Please? Just one?"

"Absolutely not."

The next day, as Becky was putting water in the tree stand, she noticed that a present for Jillian was tampered with. It had been carefully wrapped, but now had several rips that someone had attempted to repair with pieces of tape. "Jillian, did you tear the wrapping off this present to get a peek at what it was?"

With her palms up, Jillian flashed a look that she didn't know what Mom was talking about.

"Now before you say anything," warned Becky, "remember that Santa Claus knows if you've been naughty or nice."

"I'm sorry, Mommy. I peeked. I couldn't help it."

"Maybe I should take away all the presents until Christmas morning," Becky told both children. She thought a moment and added, "No, I have a better idea. For every present you try to open before Christmas, you'll wait an extra day before you can have the rest of your gifts."

"No, Mommy!" the kids cried in unison.

"All right, then. No more peeking."

On Christmas morning, the kids oohed and ahhed as they tore open their presents and flung wrapping paper until the floor was covered. Halfway through the fun, Jillian picked up a small box and said, "Here's one from Santa." After she opened it, she wrinkled her forehead and held up a shiny red collar. "Why would Santa give me this?"

"I think it's a punk-rock collar," said Tony.

Somewhat befuddled, Jillian tried to put the collar around her neck.

Austin then opened a skinny box, also from Santa, and pulled out a leash. "What's this for?" he asked.

"I think it's to keep you out of trouble," Tony replied.

By now, Becky's suspicions were all but confirmed. Under her breath, she said, "Tony, you didn't get us a you-know-what."

"I don't know what you're talking about," he replied. "Those presents are from Santa. Just like this one." He handed her a thin, square gift-wrapped box.

When she opened it, she stared at a framed photo of a blood-hound puppy. "Oh, isn't he adorable?" She showed the picture to the children.

"Daddy, whose puppy is it?" asked Austin.

"He's ours," he announced.

Becky and the kids screamed with glee. "Where is he?" asked Austin, looking behind the Christmas tree. "Where is he?"

"He's with his mommy, and he'll stay there until after the holidays," Tony explained. "Then we can bring him home."

"Oh, a bloodhound," Becky gushed, clutching the photo to her chest. "I know exactly what we'll call him. Charlie."

When the family brought Charlie home two weeks later, he proved to be a loving, gentle, long-eared sweetheart — and a challenge. The Davidsons quickly discovered that, like all blood-hound puppies, Charlie required a great deal of exercise and stimulation. "The only good puppy is a tired puppy," said Becky. Charlie followed his nose into trouble time and again. He ate a towel, a toy plastic truck, and one of Jillian's Barbie dolls. He chewed up the TV remote control and gnawed on a rocking chair that had belonged to Grandpa Charles. He dug up all the plants in the flower bed and accidentally knocked over two lamps that crashed into smithereens when he bumped into the living room end tables.

By the time he turned a year old, Charlie weighed more than one hundred pounds. He ate three times a day—that is, when he wasn't consuming whatever food and crumbs had fallen on the floor. But by then he had become an affectionate, devoted, protective member of the family. So Becky and Tony accepted the mess and the slobber that came with an ever-growing dog who loved playing in the mud and rolling in garbage—the smellier, the better.

When the next Christmas season—Charlie's first with the Davidsons—approached, Becky gave the children a short lecture on opening presents too early: "Remember what happened last year? I don't want a repeat of sneak-peeking. If I catch either one of you opening a gift or tearing the wrapping to see what's inside, I will donate it to the orphanage. Is that clear?"

"Yes, Mommy," they said.

Turning to Charlie, she added, "And that goes for you, too." The dog had sniffed several presents, but Becky and Tony were confident he had been trained to ignore all the boxes under their decorated tree.

For Christmas, Becky bought Tony a sleek, small cell phone. She put it in a box, neatly wrapped it in green-and-red paper, and placed it with the other presents. That's when she noticed that the wrapping on one of Austin's gifts was torn. "Austin, what did I tell you about peeking inside your presents?"

"I didn't do anything," the boy protested. "Honest. It was Charlie."

Becky bent down so she was at eye level with Austin. "And how did Charlie happen to select your present over all the other ones?"

"I was holding it, and he started chewing on it and . . ."

"And you just let him because you wanted to see what was on the side of the box under the wrapping." She rubbed Austin's head and chuckled. "Don't get Charlie in any more trouble, okay?"

The next day as she was tidying up the living room, Becky spotted a piece of torn wrapping paper under the couch. It was the same wrapping that she had used on Tony's gift. She walked over to the tree and picked up another piece of the same paper. Then she saw Tony's present — or what was left of it. "Oh, no!"

The wrapping paper had been torn and shredded along with the lid to the gift box. She picked up the box and looked inside. It was empty — and a little wet from drool.

Becky walked over to the bloodhound, who was lying on his side by the fireplace, snoring soundly. "Charlie, did you do this?"

Barely opening his sad eyes, he looked up at her and yawned.

"I didn't do it, Mommy," said Austin, who was watching from across the room with his sister.

"I didn't, either," Jillian piped in.

"I know you kids didn't. Our fleabag is the culprit. Charlie opened Daddy's present — I bought him a new cell phone — and hid it somewhere. Kids, help me search the house for it. It's very expensive."

They looked everywhere — behind furniture, between couch cushions, under the beds — but failed to find any trace of the phone. In frustration, Jillian confronted the dog again. "Charlie, what did you do with Daddy's Christmas present?" Charlie, who was still lounging by the fireplace, simply wagged his tail.

When Tony came home from work, Becky told him what had happened. "I wanted your gift to be a surprise," she said. "Now the only surprise is that our dog stole it, and we don't know where it is."

"We need a bloodhound to track it down," he joked.

Becky rolled her eyes, but then they lit up. "Hey, I've got an idea." She called the cell-phone company and explained her dilemma. The service representative gave her a special number to call the lost cell phone even though it hadn't been activated.

When Becky hung up, she told her family, "Okay, I'm going to call the number. Let's be real quiet and listen for the ring tones."

When she called the number, they all heard a faint ringing. "It's coming from the fireplace," said Austin.

"No, it sounds like it's underneath Charlie," said Jillian. She shoved the dog until he slowly rose and moved a few steps. The cell phone was not where he had been resting, yet everyone could still hear it.

"I think the ringing is coming from *inside* Charlie!" exclaimed Becky. She dropped to all fours and put her ear next to his ample belly. The ring tones were definitely louder there. "Oh, no! The darn dog swallowed the phone!"

Through the folds around his sleepy eyes, Charlie appeared somewhat puzzled because everyone was staring at him in astonishment.

"I don't believe it!" Tony muttered.

For about five seconds, no one said a word. The only sounds were the ring tones emitting from Charlie's stomach. Jillian and Austin began to giggle, then Becky and Tony did, too, before everyone burst out in laughter. Soon they were hooting and howling and doubled over, trying to catch their breath.

Charlie looked bewildered and a little scared. He had never seen them act like this before. And what was with the ringing in his stomach?

The Davidsons took their "phoney" bloodhound to the animal clinic. After examining the dog and taking X-rays, the veterinarian concluded there was no need to operate. "The phone is small, and Charlie's intestines are big, so he should be able to pass it soon," the vet said. He gave the dog a laxative to help speed up the process.

The next day, after Charlie did his business, Becky retrieved the cell phone. It was in perfect working order, but she turned it in for a new one for Tony's Christmas present. She didn't want her husband to have a phone that had answered nature's call.

The Hanukkah Surprise

"Please, Daddy, please!" begged Libby Wechter. "Please can we get a kitten for Hanukkah?"

"Now, Libby, what did I tell you?" Aaron Wechter said with a trace of annoyance. "I've made it clear that I don't want a cat in the house. I'm not fond of them. They're sneaky and destructive and have a mind of their own."

"Yeah, a stubborn mind just like yours," said the ten-year-old girl with a pout. As soon as the words left her tongue, Libby realized her mistake. She knew better than to be rude to her dad, whose burly six-foot-two-inch frame and booming voice could intimidate anyone in the neighborhood, let alone a ponytailed fourth grader. "I'm sorry, Daddy. I didn't mean it."

Aaron bent over until he was face-to-face with Libby and said, "Let me give you a piece of advice, honey: Insulting your dad isn't a smart way to win him over."

Although Libby's mother, Rachel, and six-year-old twin brothers, Ethan and Ira, had lobbied for a cat, Aaron had put his foot down. There would be no feline pet in the house. He had his reasons, but they weren't the ones that he had given his family.

Aaron headed a small construction company that was building a warehouse in the outskirts of Saint Paul, Minnesota. As a hands-on boss, Aaron worked side by side with his crew on the project. The walls were up and the roof was completed just in time before a wintry mix of wind-whipped snow and sleet struck the area.

Shortly before Hanukkah arrived, Aaron and his crew were eating lunch in the half-completed warehouse when they heard a mournful meow coming from behind a stack of lumber. One of the men, Turk Lewis, went to investigate and returned holding a mewing brown, white, and orange fur ball in his meaty hands. "Look what I found," he said. "The poor thing. She's shaking like a leaf. I think she's one of those calicats."

"Calico," Aaron muttered, barely looking at the kitten. "There's no such thing as a calicat."

Turk put the kitten down, and she ran to a spot where worker Lars Norberg had tossed a piece of his turkey sandwich. She gobbled it up and meowed for more. "She's really hungry," he said, giving her another piece. "I wonder where she came from."

"Could be anywhere," said Turk. "She could be lost or abandoned or left her mama."

"Hey, Aaron," said Lars. "Why don't you take the kitten home to your kids?"

"Absolutely not," said Aaron, paying no attention to the kitten. "Come on. Let's get back to work."

At the end of the day, the workers headed for their trucks, leaving the kitty to fend for herself. Over the next few days, the kitten appeared regularly around noon and begged for food, so the men fed her scraps from their lunches. Seeing the way Aaron ignored the kitty and refused to feed her, the workers assumed their boss hated cats. They also noticed he changed the subject whenever they talked about the kitten.

On Friday, the first day of Hanukkah, Aaron told his men, "We're going to knock off early today because of Hanukkah, but you'll get full pay. And, yes, I know none of you are Jewish like me, so consider it part of your Christmas bonus."

"Just what is Hanukkah, boss?" asked Lars.

"It's a Jewish holiday that lasts eight days. More than two thousand years ago, when Syria controlled what is now Israel, the Jews' religion was banned, and their temple in Jerusalem was looted. When the Maccabees—a Jewish liberation movement—rose up and defeated the Syrians, the temple was nearly in ruins. There was only enough consecrated oil in the lamp to fuel the eternal flame in the temple for one day. But, miraculously, it burned for eight days, until more oil was brought in.

"To commemorate this miracle, Jews celebrate Hanukkah. We light a candle each night for eight nights in a special holder called a menorah. And each night we give a blessing, sing songs, play games, and exchange gifts, mostly for the children."

"My kids would like to be Jewish just so they could get gifts for eight nights instead of just on Christmas," joked Turk.

Early in the afternoon, Aaron sent everyone home and was the last to leave the warehouse. He got into his pickup, started the engine, and then stepped back outside to scrape away the crusty snow that had formed on the windshield. He left the driver's side door partially open.

As he cleared the windshield, he thought he heard mewing, but he didn't see anything. Then he hopped into his truck, put it in gear, and drove off. He had driven about one hundred feet when he felt something brush up against his ankle. "Yikes! A mouse!" He slammed on his brakes, causing the pickup to spin a half circle in the parking lot.

Aaron looked down on the floor and said, "You're not a mouse." Crouched by the accelerator was the calico kitten — the same one his men had been feeding at lunch. "How did you get in here?"

He picked up the calico, who was shivering and purring at the same time. She didn't meow or hiss or flash her sharp claws. Instead she leaped out of his grasp and onto his jacket, then burrowed her head by his neck.

"My gosh, you look just like Kaya," he said as his eyes began to water. He whipped off his gloves and placed his big calloused hands gently on the kitten and stroked her. He couldn't believe that this calico had the identical color and markings as his beloved childhood pet. She had the same white streak from her nose to her forehead, the same brown and orange splotches on her sides, and the same black and gray rings on her tail.

Memories of his long-ago pet flashed in his mind: Kaya sprawled on the kitchen table watching him do his homework . . . Kaya playfully knocking knickknacks off shelves . . . Kaya sleeping above his head on his pillow . . . Kaya batting his nose to wake him up . . . Kaya chasing a tennis ball around his room . . . Kaya curled up in his lap while he watched television.

She was the one constant in his childhood following his parents' divorce. When his mother became extremely ill and was in and out of the hospital, Aaron was shuffled from one relative to another. He didn't have many friends, but at least he always had Kaya by his side, giving him comfort and making him laugh. For ten years, they had an unbreakable bond until that awful day.

It still hurt to think about it after all these years: He was holding Kaya on the front stoop of his aunt's house — his fourth home in the previous seven years — when the neighbor's big dog got loose and charged at Aaron and his cat. Kaya yowled, leaped out of the boy's arms, and fled in terror, the dog in hot pursuit. She dashed into the street, right into the path of a moving car. The driver swerved and braked, but not in time. Kaya lay on the pavement, dead. Aaron was so devastated that he vowed never to get attached to another pet again. Ever. He felt he couldn't stand the pain of losing an animal close to his heart.

That's why he had refused the pleas of his children for a cat and why for days he wanted nothing to do with this stray calico. Yet here he was in his truck, a thirty-two-year-old man choked up over the loss of a childhood cat while petting a kitten that looked as if she could have been Kaya's twin.

Let her go, he told himself. *She's just a stray. Don't hold her. You'll bond with her and just get hurt again. At the very most, take her to the shelter and let them deal with her. But the shelter is on the other side of town and it's snowing hard. I better go home.* "Okay," he said to the kitten, "you can stay with me — but just for the night. Tomorrow, I'll drop you off at the shelter."

The kitten purred, snuggled in his lap, and went to sleep. On the way home, Aaron passed a pet-supplies store. *I'm definitely not stopping here,* he told himself. But his hands on the steering wheel acted otherwise, and the truck turned in to the parking lot. *I don't believe I'm doing this. I'm going to regret it.*

A half hour later, he arrived home carrying a small white box with a blue bow. "Happy Hanukkah, everyone!" When Rachel, Libby, Ira, and Ethan crowded around, Aaron kneeled down and opened the box. The kitten hopped out, triggering a round of happy screams from the overjoyed children. After the initial battle of who got to hold the kitten the longest, the kids settled down because they didn't want to frighten her. The family considered dozens of names before deciding on Libby's suggestion to call her Ariel — a name spelled out with the first letter of each of the Wechters' names.

Of course, there was no way Aaron could take the kitten to the shelter now, not after the reception Ariel received from his family. The next day, Rachel took the kitten to the veterinarian, who estimated that she was four months old and needed several shots and some medicine to clear up a few minor health problems.

No kitten was given more love and kindness than Ariel was — at least for the first month. Everyone took turns feeding her, playing with her, cleaning out her litter box, and sleeping with her. But with schoolwork, Libby's ballet and guitar lessons, and the twins' basketball games and karate lessons, the kids were too busy to give much attention to the calico.

But that was okay with Ariel, because she had already chosen her favorite human. She was Aaron's pet. Although she spent time with the kids, she liked to sleep on his lap while he read. She learned tricks from him in exchange for treats and soon wowed guests by doing backflips off the coffee table and by jumping through a hoop.

Raised as a house cat, Ariel was extremely curious and bold — and found herself in the strangest places. The family discovered this trait of hers a few months after she adopted them. It happened during one of her evening rituals.

"If you want some cheese, you have to ask politely," Aaron told her.

Ariel meowed three times and then danced in a circle in the kitchen.

"Since you put it that way, okay." He opened the refrigerator, took out a hunk of cheese, and placed it on the counter. He grabbed a knife, cut off a piece, put the rest back in the refrigerator, and closed the door. After washing off the knife, he looked down, expecting to see the cat.

"Where did you go? Hey, Ariel, I have cheese for you." He called out to her, but there was no answer. He went into the family room, then down the hall and looked in the mudroom, where her litter box was kept, but she was nowhere to be found. "Rachel, have you seen Ariel?"

"No, but I heard a strange noise a minute ago," she replied. "I thought it was coming from under the breakfast table, but I didn't see anything." They heard a muffled yowl and the clanking of bottles. "There it is again."

"It sounds like it's coming from the refrigerator," Aaron said.

He opened the door. "Ariel!" From the fridge's middle shelf, Ariel stared at Aaron and meowed before jumping into his arms. He laughed. "You're one cool cat — literally."

As he started to close the door, he spotted the cheese in the refrigerator. Ariel had pulled the plastic wrap off the cheese and taken a few bites. "It's obvious you'll stop at nothing to get your cheese."

Since then, Ariel had been found in kitchen cabinets, in the kids' toy chest, an open desk drawer, the clothes dryer, and a dozen other weird hiding places.

As Hanukkah neared the following year, Rachel was busy wrapping presents. She had bought Aaron a big backpack for backcountry camping and found a large box to put it in. As Rachel started to wrap the gift, Ariel was leaping on the paper and tearing it up. "Ariel! Go away. Shoo! Shoo!" ordered Rachel as she bopped the cat gently on the rear end with an empty wrapping paper tube. The calico scurried off.

Rachel finished wrapping the presents and then, with the kids' help, made latkes (potato pancakes) and jelly doughnuts, traditional holiday foods. When Aaron came home, he chatted with Rachel and the kids. "Where's Ariel?" he asked.

"She's around here somewhere," said Libby. "She was messing with the pencils on my desk this afternoon."

"She got into the wrapping paper, too," Rachel added.

Aaron called out to Ariel. "I've got cheese waiting for you. Ariel, come here, girl." When there was no response, he shrugged. "She must be in one of her moods. Maybe she's sulking because everyone was telling her to go away."

Normally, she would have shown up for dinner, because she always begged under the table. It usually paid off for her, but tonight she was a no-show. By bedtime, the family was worried about her. They searched the closets, garage, and basement. They checked the bookshelves, kitchen cabinets, and chests of drawers, all without success. Everyone was certain she hadn't slipped out of the house.

"Maybe she's sick and hiding somewhere in the house," Aaron said. "Cats will do that, you know."

"What if she's dead?" asked Libby.

"She looked healthy and frisky as ever today when I last saw her," said Rachel.

"With any luck, she'll show up in the morning," said Aaron.

He didn't sleep well that night. He kept waiting to hear that friendly meow. All the time he wondered, *Where could she be? What if she did get out? It's in the twenties outside. She could freeze to death.*

In the morning, he checked her food bowl. It hadn't been touched. Neither had her litter box. "I'm afraid she's either dead or she sneaked out of the house when one of us opened the door and didn't notice," Aaron told the family. "I think she's gone for good." His voice cracked, but he immediately cleared his throat. Kissing his wife and kids, he headed for the door and said, "Let's cheer up. Tonight is the first night of Hanukkah."

"It won't be the same without Ariel," Libby whimpered.

On his way to work, Aaron thought, *Darn it, I should never have brought home that cat. I knew better. I knew it would hurt if something bad happened to her. And now it has. And it hurts.*

He was hoping for a phone call from Rachel telling him that Ariel had been found alive and well. But the only call he received from her was to pick up some *rugelach* (pastries) on his way home.

A half hour after sundown, the family lit the first candle on the menorah and gave a blessing. At dinner, Libby offered another blessing and added, "Dear God, can you please bring Ariel home to us? We miss her."

No more was said about the missing cat. After eating, they played dreidel, a game of chance with a top marked with four Hebrew letters. Sitting around the table, everyone put a chocolate coin in the center, known as the pot. Then one person spun the dreidel. Depending on the letter it landed on, the person either collected all the coins in the pot, half, none, or had to add a coin. They took turns spinning the dreidel. Whenever the pot was empty, they all had to add a coin.

Then it came time for each to open one gift. Libby got a camera, the boys their own walkie-talkies, and Rachel a necklace. When it was Aaron's turn, he opened the big box and said, "I have absolutely no idea what's inside." He was definitely right about that. As he peered inside, he burst into tearful laughter. "What a perfect gift! It's just what I wanted! It's what we all wanted!"

Rachel, Libby, and the twins traded quizzical looks. *Gee, he's making a big deal over a backpack,* thought Rachel. *And why would he say it's something we all wanted?*

Aaron reached into the box and pulled out . . .

"Ariel!" screamed Rachel and the kids.

The cat meowed and yipped as if to say, "What took you so long to find me?" Then she ran to each person, demanding they shower her with love.

"Why, that little stinker," said Rachel. "She was such a pain when I was wrapping your gift that I shooed her away. Obviously, she sneaked behind me and jumped into the box, and I didn't know it when I sealed it up. So she's been in there for more than twenty-four hours."

"It's a good thing this was my gift on the first day of Hanukkah," said Aaron. "If you had given this to me on the last day, Ariel would have been stuck in there for eight days."

"That," cracked Libby, "would have been a *cat*-astrophe!"

The Undersea Reindeer

As his submarine docked for repairs at the harbor of Polyarny in the far northwest corner of the Soviet Union, Commander Geoffrey Sladen stood on the bridge and buttoned the collar of his coat.

It was a cold, blustery, overcast day in 1941 — one that reminded him of winter in London, where he wished he was right now. He worried about his wife, Sarah, and their three children, and wondered how they were coping without him in their war-ravaged country.

As commander of H.M.S. *Trident*, he had been at sea for nearly six months and missed his family terribly. But Great Britain was fighting for its life against Germany as World War II entered its third year, and he had a job to do.

Sladen's vessel was part of a fleet of British submarines defending merchant ships that carried badly needed supplies to the Soviet Union, an important ally of Great Britain. The *Trident* also patrolled the seas off the Norwegian coast, hunting for German ships to torpedo. During one sea battle, the submarine sank an enemy supply ship but suffered damage to one of its engines from the blast of a German depth charge.

The sub made it safely to Polyarny, where repairs were expected to take about a week. From the vessel's bridge, Sladen allowed himself a moment to forget about the war and daydream about his loving family.

If I do nothing else on shore leave, he thought, *I must get Sarah something nice for Christmas.* It was only October, but Sladen liked to plan ahead. He thought about getting her authentic wooden Russian Easter eggs—delicately painted faces and scenes on egg shaped wood with a shiny lacquer finish. *Maybe she would like a porcelain animal figure or a blown-glass vase.*

But Sladen never got the chance to shop. He was too busy overseeing the repair work and plotting strategy with Soviet navy officials, especially Admiral Vladimir Petrovich. The two developed a quick friendship, and on the night before the *Trident* was to head out to sea, Sladen accepted the admiral's invitation to dinner at the Russian's home.

They talked mostly about the war, of course, but during the meal, the subject of Christmas came up.

"It is my most favorite time of year," said Sladen. "I have such great memories as a child, waiting for the arrival of Father Christmas. And now that I have young children of my own, I read them an American poem called 'A Visit from Saint Nicholas.'" The commander closed his eyes, smiled, and recited a passage from that classic poem:

"With a little old driver so lively and quick,
I knew in a moment it must be Saint Nick.
More rapid than eagles, his coursers they came,
And he whistled and shouted and called them by name:
'Now, Dasher! Now, Dancer! Now, Prancer and Vixen!
On, Comet! On, Cupid! On, Donner and Blitzen!
To the top of the porch! To the top of the wall!
Now dash away! Dash away! Dash away all!'"

Petrovich applauded Sladen and joined him in a hearty laugh.

"We have our own Saint Nick or, as you call him, Father Christmas," said the admiral. "Here in the Soviet Union, we call him Ded Moroz. That translates in English to Grandfather Frost. He brings presents to children. However, unlike Father Christmas arriving at children's homes in a flying sleigh, Grandfather Frost brings the gifts in person. And he comes on New Year's Day, not Christmas Day. It is a wonderful time. Families gather around the *yolka* and . . ."

"What's that?" asked Sladen. "A giant egg yolk?"

Petrovich chuckled. "A *yolka* is our version of a Christmas tree decorated with homemade ornaments and fruit and candy. Sometimes, for the smaller children, Grandfather Frost places gifts under the New Year tree with the help of Snegurochka, his granddaughter. She's better known as the Snow Maiden. She's dressed in white fur and is beautiful."

"What does Grandfather Frost look like?" Sladen asked.

"He has a long white beard. He wears a fur-lined blue coat and matching hat and big black boots. He walks with a long magical staff and rides in a *troika*. That's a sled drawn by three horses."

Petrovich pointed to the bowl in front of Sladen. "In our house, we make a big pot of *kutya*, which is what you're eating right now."

"It's very good," said the commander, after taking a big sip from his spoon. "It's like a vegetarian porridge."

"That's exactly what it is. My cook has put various types of wheat and grain in it and sweetened it with honey."

With a sly grin, Petrovich said, "Here's what we do on Christmas Eve when we eat kutya." To Sladen's stunned amazement, the admiral flung a spoonful of kutya toward the ceiling. A big gob stuck on a wooden beam above the table. "Ah-ha!" Petrovich beamed. "The kutya sticks. That's a good omen for the future. Perhaps it means we will win this awful war."

Sladen eyed the glob, calculating in his head exactly where the blob of porridge would land when it peeled off the beam. *I think it will fall into the bowl of boiled potatoes.*

"Go ahead," urged the admiral. "Try it."

"Oh, I couldn't."

"I insist. It's tradition."

"Well, okay." Feeling like a schoolboy about to fire a spitball across the classroom, Sladen scooped a hefty spoonful of *kutya*. Whipping his arm in an underhand motion, he sent the goop flying past the beam and watched it splatter on the ceiling. "It's holding!"

"Bravo, Commander! We are sure to win the war now!"

The dinner conversation returned to more serious matters as the two consumed kutya, salted herring, pickled cucumbers, potatoes, and fried sturgeon.

At the end of the meal, Petrovich said, "I hope you don't mind that we ate no meat."

"That is perfectly fine, Admiral. I enjoyed the food immensely and am so grateful for your hospitality."

"In my country, I am considered strange. I think in your country I would be called a nutter, a crazy person. I eat seafood and fowl, but I can't bring myself to consume red meat of any kind. That is unusual because I own a small reindeer farm. I sell reindeer milk, but I will not sell a reindeer to be slaughtered for its food or hide or antlers. I will sell them only to people who will use them to pull sleighs or to get milk.

"In the Soviet Union, most reindeer are treated like cattle. They are allowed to graze, and then they are slaughtered. I get laughed at by my fellow officers because I won't kill reindeer. They think I am getting soft. They don't respect reindeer the way you do in Great Britain." He grinned. "At least, you have them flying through the air and pulling Father Christmas's sleigh."

"Yes, reindeer are looked at favorably in my country," said Sladen. "In fact, when Christmas comes, no one would dare hurt a reindeer. They are an important part of the holiday. My children even know the personalities of Father Christmas's reindeer. Dasher is the speediest and Dancer the most graceful. Prancer is the most powerful while Vixen is the prettiest. Comet brings children wonder and Cupid brings love. As for Donner and Blitzen, they are pretty rowdy and known as thunder and lightning."

Just then, the glob of kutya that Sladen had tossed to the ceiling came loose and splashed right into his glass of wine.

"Ha! Ha! A direct hit." Petrovich chortled.

"Let's hope that's an omen for the *Trident*'s torpedoes," said Sladen. "I would love to score some direct hits on the German ships."

Getting up from the table, the admiral said, "Come, let us sit by the fire. Your children, you have pictures of them?"

Sladen flipped open his billfold and pulled out a photo of his three children — George, seven; Amanda, five; and Elizabeth, one.

"Such handsome children," marveled Petrovich. "Alas, I have none of my own."

"And here is a photo of my wife, Sarah," said Sladen. "She and our children live with her parents on a small farm near Scotland, away — I hope — from any bombing. The children love the animals so much. My family likes living there, although it's a little more icy and snowy than in London. Last winter, when Elizabeth was born, Sarah had a nasty time trying to push the pram [baby buggy] in all the snow."

As Sladen talked about his family, the admiral seemed in deep thought for a few seconds before a twinkle came to his eyes. A moment later, he changed the subject. "When do you expect to return to your home port?"

"In two weeks. We will be cruising off the Norwegian coast on our way back, looking to attack any German ships in the area."

After a final toast for the success of the Allies, Sladen got up to leave. "Admiral, I can't begin to tell you what a wonderful time I had tonight. The food and company were terrific. I enjoyed talking about Christmas traditions, too, although I confess it made me feel a little homesick."

"May you have a safe voyage home — and sink a few German ships along the way."

The next morning, the commander was aboard the *Trident*, going over the latest orders from the Royal Navy with his officers. Meanwhile, crewmen were loading the last of the supplies for the trip home. Sladen paid no attention to the five-foot-by-four-foot wooden crate that was carried aboard by two Russian sailors.

Hours later, the sub slipped away from Polyarny and into the icy gray waters of the Barents Sea. It headed past the northern tip of Finland and toward the western coast of Norway.

"Captain," said first mate Scotty Williams. "We have a crate in the supply room that's making a weird noise."

"What kind of weird noise?" asked Sladen.

"Thumping and whinnying, sir."

"So, why haven't you opened it up?"

"Well, sir, the crate is addressed to you personally."

"To me? I didn't order anything."

Sladen followed Williams to the supply room and studied the crate, which had several tiny holes. An unpleasant odor was coming out of them.

"Open it up. Hurry," Sladen ordered, his curiosity heightened.

Williams and another crewman used a crowbar and opened the front of the crate. Their jaws dropped in astonishment when they looked inside.

"What the . . . ?"

"Blimey!"

"What in the world is that?"

From inside peeked two big brown eyes, one on each side of a long, dark gray snout. Triangular-shaped ears were bent sideways on a gray head that was cocked to the side. Beanpolelike legs held up a slender, fuzzy body.

"I don't believe this," Sladen muttered. "It's a baby reindeer!"

On the other side of the crate was taped an envelope addressed to the commander. He opened it up and read the note: "Father Christmas has his reindeer, and now you and your family shall have one, too. It will make pushing your pram easier in the snow. Cheers and a happy Christmas. Vladimir."

Sladen had always been cool under fire and had a reputation for making snap decisions. But this time he was speechless.

"Captain, what are we going to do with it?" asked Williams. "Can we butcher it, cook it, and eat it?"

Sladen glared at him. "No, of course not. We'll keep it."

"Begging your pardon, sir. But it's a reindeer . . . on a submarine. Doesn't that sound a little . . . I don't know . . . *bizarre?*"

"It's a Christmas gift. We will keep it as our mascot until we get back to port. The reindeer will be with us for only a couple of weeks."

Accompanying the crate was a smaller box that contained moss, lichen, and grass for the animal to eat on its journey to Great Britain.

"Well, let her out," Sladen ordered. "Get her some food and water."

As word spread throughout the submarine, the fifty-five-man crew had mixed feelings. Some didn't think it was appropriate. Some wanted to kill and eat it. But most thought it was pretty neat to have a reindeer on board. They even suggested names for their new mascot: Rupert. Randolph. Roland. But those names were nixed because the animal was a female.

After some thought, Sladen picked out her name. "She came from Polyarny, so let's call her Pollyanna." It was a play on the name of the port as well as the title of the beloved children's book *Pollyanna*. That story, which he had read to his kids, was about a young orphan girl who brightens the lives of those around her by always finding a reason to feel glad no matter how awful the situation.

"Aye, aye, Captain!" said Williams. "Pollyanna, it is."

And so Pollyanna, who slept on a blanket on the floor in the cramped captain's quarters, became the first and only reindeer to live in a submarine. Over the next few days, those crewmen who didn't want the animal aboard soon changed their minds because she was sweet. The adopted calf—a baby reindeer is called a calf, not a fawn—was allowed to stroll through the sub and always brought a smile to the men. There was one thing they didn't like about her—she wasn't potty-trained. The sailors drew cards to see who had to clean up behind her. The smelly job fell to the man with the lowest card.

Every evening when the klaxon made its *ka-hoo-ga* sound to signal that the submarine was surfacing, Pollyanna rushed from her cabin. She stood under the hatch, waiting for someone to open it so she could catch a breath of fresh air. She hogged the spot, often nudging other crewmen away. The only person she let near the hatch was the captain, with whom she had formed a bond.

After one week at sea, the *Trident* received new orders: The sub was to patrol the Norwegian Sea between Iceland and Norway for an additional thirty days. The crew groaned when they heard the news. Trotting out the reindeer, Sladen told his men, "Just like her namesake, let's find the plus side to every bad situation. For us, that means more opportunities to sink an enemy ship."

No one knew how Pollyanna would react in a sea battle. The crew realized she couldn't be ambling around the sub when all hands were busy, so Sladen ordered her locked in his cabin during combat.

After the second week at sea, Pollyanna had eaten all the food that came with her, so the crew fed her scraps from the mess hall, which she enjoyed. She also developed a special liking for evaporated milk.

When the *Trident* arrived in England four weeks later than planned, relatives of the crew were waiting at the dock. Sladen greeted his family with big bear hugs before announcing, "I know it's only November, but I brought you all an early Christmas present that I'm sure you'll never forget."

Just then first mate Williams came over and whispered in Sladen's ear, "Uh, Captain, we have a problem."

"What's the matter?"

The first mate turned his back to Sladen's family and said quietly, "Well, sir, it's Pollyanna. She grew a lot while we were at sea, and now we can't get her out of the hatch."

Sladen stroked his chin and then said, "Okay, here's what to do: Get some of the crew and lay down Pollyanna. While they hold her, tie her legs under her belly. She'll put up a struggle, but it's the only way. Once she's trussed up, they should be able to carry her out."

"Honey, is something wrong?" asked Sladen's wife, Sarah.

Sladen faced her and said, "A minor glitch, sweetheart. Now then, what was I talking about?"

"A Christmas present!" shouted Amanda and George in unison.

"Ah, yes. I brought you something from the Soviet Union. It should be here soon."

A short while later, Williams, holding a rope looped around the reindeer's neck, gently led the animal down the gangplank and onto the dock.

"Merry Christmas!" cried Sladen to his family.

"Geoffrey, what is it?" asked Sarah.

"A reindeer," Sladen replied. "For you. For all of you."

The kids shrieked with delight and rushed up to the reindeer and petted her.

"Her name is Pollyanna," Sladen said. "And she's ours—a gift from Admiral Petrovich. He said she would be perfect for pulling Elizabeth's pram."

"Oh, darling, I do love the idea, but where will we keep her?" Sarah asked.

"On your parents' farm, of course. She would be free to roam and . . ."

"We can't, sweetheart. While you were away, the Royal Air Force took over the farm to use the land for training. We've moved into a small house in Berwick."

"What will we do, Daddy?" asked Amanda, her lips beginning to tremble. "We can't just turn her loose."

"Well, let's think," said Sladen. "Remember in the book *Pollyanna*? She always found the silver lining in everything."

"I have an idea," George said. "Why don't we give her to Father Christmas? Pollyanna won't feel so alone because she will be with all the other reindeer."

"That's a wonderful suggestion," said Sladen. "But until we can contact Father Christmas, I think Pollyanna will be better off at the London Zoo."

And so the family presented the zoo with a living, breathing Christmas gift.

"I'm sad we couldn't keep her," said Amanda on the way home. "But the zoo people are happy."

"I feel good about it," George added. "It's strange, though. The best Christmas present we ever got is the one we gave away."

For decades, the tale of Pollyanna was considered nothing more than a legend of World War II, because the real facts had long been forgotten. Besides, who would believe that a reindeer lived for weeks aboard a British submarine during wartime? But in 2001, the Royal Navy Submarine Museum in Gosport, Hampshire, England, was given a picture of the late Trident skipper Geoffrey

Sladen with Pollyanna the reindeer. The photograph was found when the submariner's family cleaned out old papers and sent them to the museum.

Further checking revealed that a Russian admiral had given Pollyanna as a Christmas gift to Sladen, who then donated her to the zoo. The reindeer adjusted easily to her spacious new surroundings, which were much more comfortable than in a submarine. However, she never forgot her time under the sea. Whenever she heard the clanging bell of a fire engine going past the zoo, she would lower her head just as she did when she heard the submarine's klaxon. Pollyanna lived at the zoo until her death in 1946, which occurred only a few days after the Trident was decommissioned.

The Christmas Day Miracle

Cap the border collie sniffed the salty sea air and then raced after two seagulls that had the gall to land twenty feet away from him. The birds waited until the black-and-white dog was only two feet away before lifting off, protesting with loud squawks.

The Reverend Gavin Walker and his wife, Jo, laughed at their dog. "You would think that after all the years we've been coming here, Cap would know that he's never going to catch a bird," said Gavin.

"Those birds just love to torment him," added Jo.

On this breezy fall day in 2001, Cap and the Walkers were hiking on a scenic path along the top of the three-hundred-foot-high sandstone cliffs of Saint Bees Head on the coast of northwest England. The waves crashed into the red rocks below, making thunderous roars. The Walkers, both in their late fifties, were bundled up with scarves and gloves as they watched Cap romp ahead, chasing birds and sniffing for rabbits. He loved to frolic on the vast, flat, grassy top of Saint Bees.

But Cap's life hadn't always been so nice. Born on a farm, he was expected to become a sheep herder because that's what border collies are known for. But his instinct to herd didn't measure up to the standards that his original owner demanded. The young dog was ignored by the farmer's family and became a canine outcast who had to fend for himself. He stole food wherever and whenever he could from the pigsty and the goat pen.

Some of the farmhands didn't treat him any better. On their way to hunt rabbits and squirrels, they deliberately fired their weapons to scare and torment the dog, turning him into a nervous wreck. Fortunately, the teenage son of the farm owner could no longer tolerate this cruelty toward the unhappy dog. He coaxed the border collie into his truck and took him to a shelter for abandoned and abused animals.

The dog remained there for several months. One day the Walkers, who were hoping to adopt a pet, went to the animal shelter. As they ambled past the kennels of barking dogs, Jo spotted the shaggy-haired border collie. Looking into the eyes of the two-year-old dog, Jo saw in him a spunky, smart survivor. "He's the one we want," she announced. "I just know he's going to be a great companion." And so the Walkers brought the dog home and named him Captain — Cap for short.

It took a while for the couple and dog to bond, because Cap needed constant reassurance they wouldn't abandon him. Once he saw how much they loved and nurtured him, the dog returned the favor with his loyalty and devotion.

Of all the things Cap loved to do with the Walkers, none pleased him more than going for long strolls with Jo and Gavin. One of the dog's favorite places for an outing together was at Saint Bees Head, which was a thirty-minute walk from their home.

At Saint Bees, the majestic red cliffs support the largest sea-bird colony in the region. In spring and summer, guillemots, kittiwakes, fulmars, and razorbills flutter noisily around while ravens and peregrines soar above the rocky shoreline. Every time he visited there, Cap tried to chase them all. He had yet to catch one.

On this windy fall day, the Walkers ambled along the main path, which passed by the remains of several old coal mines and quarries. Cap galloped ahead of them on another one of his fruitless pursuits. Before Cap ran too far ahead, Gavin whistled at the dog, who abruptly put on his brakes and trotted back to them. "Good boy," praised Jo.

The three of them stayed on the path as it turned away from the cliff and curved inland and down a slight slope until they lost sight of the sea. About one hundred yards ahead, four teenage boys were kneeling on the ground. Cap began to growl, which was unusual because he liked most everyone. "What is it, Cap?" asked Jo. She looked around and didn't see anything to cause concern. Cap kept his eyes focused on the teenagers and continued to growl. "Oh, they're harmless, Cap."

Just then, the boys bolted, leaving behind several small objects burning and glowing on the ground. Suddenly, they exploded in a rapid series of bangs, booms, and pops.

Jo was so startled she almost lost her breath.

"It's okay," assured Gavin. "They're just harmless fireworks."

But it wasn't okay to Cap. The deafening bangs sounded like the gunshots he used to hear on the farm when the workers terrorized him. The dog let out a frantic yelp and scampered off in the opposite direction toward the cliffs.

"Cap! Cap! Come back!" Jo yelled.

Gavin let loose with a loud whistle, but nothing could stop the dog from fleeing as the fireworks continued to erupt. "Come on, Jo," the reverend said. "We'd better go after him."

By now, Cap had dashed over the rise and was out of sight. The Walkers hustled as fast as they could. When they reached the rise, they were troubled because they couldn't see Cap anywhere between them and the cliffs. Jo scanned the grassy area, which was empty except for the few people who were strolling on the path. "Where could he be?" she asked.

"I don't know, but let's ask everyone we see."

The first three people questioned by the Walkers said they hadn't seen Cap. The fourth, an elderly woman, said, "Oh, my dears, I don't know if I should say this, but I saw a black-and-white dog running toward the sea. I was distracted for only a second by a seagull. When I looked for the dog again, he was gone."

Tears clouded Jo's eyes, and she gripped her husband's arm. "You don't think Cap could have fallen . . ." She couldn't finish her sentence because the thought was too horrible to consider.

"Stay here and let me go to the edge and look," Gavin said, his stomach twisting in a knot over the possibility.

"No, I'll go with you. I have to see for myself." The couple held hands to give each other support as they walked to the edge of the cliff. They knew that if Cap fell, he would have been killed by the impact of plunging onto the rocks. Even if, by some incredible luck, he survived the fall, they believed he would have been battered to death by the pounding waves or would have drowned in the rough seas. The Walkers hesitantly peered down at the rocky shore below, expecting to see a sickening sight. An angry surf slammed into the rocks, spewing towers of water against the sides of the cliff. But wherever the couple looked, there was no sign of Cap's body.

"Do you think there's any chance he survived?" Jo asked.

Gavin sighed and shook his head. "I'm afraid not. We would have seen him."

"So why haven't we spotted his body?"

"It's possible the waves carried it out to sea."

"It's also possible that he didn't fall off. No one actually saw him fall. Gavin, I don't want to give up yet. Let's keep searching. Maybe he's so scared by the fireworks that he's hiding somewhere along the cliff."

The reverend and his wife scoured the area for hours. They called Cap's name and whistled for him, but to no avail. As the afternoon light began to fade, Jo said, "I can't leave. If he's alive, he might come out of hiding and won't know where to find us. I think we should spend the night here."

Gavin agreed. He hurried back to their home in nearby Egremont and returned with food, camping gear, and a tent. They set up camp near the spot where they had lost him and stayed there through the night. When morning arrived, there was still no sign of the dog anywhere on top, on the cliff ledges, or on the rocky shore below.

The Walkers searched for several more days but finally gave up. "It's time we admit to ourselves that Cap has died," Gavin told Jo. "He certainly would have shown up by now, and if someone had found him, they would have looked at his dog tags and called us."

"I suppose you're right," said Jo. In a trembling voice, she blurted, "But I miss him so much." She broke down in sobs. "He was such a wonderful dog."

As the weeks went by, there wasn't a night that Jo didn't think about the loss of her beloved Cap. But by early December, she turned her attention to the holidays — a time when she had to decorate the rectory and help with the Christmas program at church.

About a week before the holiday, Gavin and Jo were having dinner. Gavin seemed in an especially good mood, although he constantly kept looking at his watch and then out the dining room window. "You know what I like most about the holidays?" he told Jo. "The surprises, the unexpected gifts, and the happy reactions on the faces of those who receive them."

Moments later, the doorbell rang and Gavin sprang from his chair. From the foyer, he called out, "Jo, can you come here, please? There's someone I want you to meet."

As Jo walked down the hall toward the foyer, she saw that Gavin had his camera trained on her. "What's going on?" she asked.

Suddenly, from behind his legs bounded a black-and-white border collie puppy with a big red bow around its neck. Jo shrieked in delight. "A puppy! For me?" As Gavin snapped pictures, she scooped up the little dog and hugged it. The pup responded by licking her cheek and uttering sweet little yelps. "Oh, it's so precious!"

"It's a he," said Gavin. "I wanted to give him to you on Christmas Day, but I just couldn't wait any longer. Merry Christmas, sweetheart."

"Where did you get him?"

"I heard that the animal shelter had taken in a border collie and her litter, so I went down there and arranged to adopt the pick of the litter. One of the workers there dropped him off tonight. I know how much you miss Cap, and I thought this would cheer you up."

"Oh, he's just too cute for words. In the spirit of Christmas, I think I'll name him after one of the three wise men — Gaspar."

Jo was thrilled. She had a new dog to love — a dog that she hoped would someday get rid of the ache in her heart over the loss of Cap.

A few days later, Jo read a draft of the sermon that Gavin would give on Christmas morning. It was titled "The Magic of Christmas." The sermon said that for believers in the miracle of the birth of Jesus, the impossible can become the possible in faith and in life.

When Jo finished reading his sermon, she told him, "Gavin, this is beautiful. Anything *is* possible. You truly are a wise man."

"Why, thank you. And I don't even have any gold, frankincense, or myrrh."

As she put up the final Christmas decorations at the main entrance to the church, Jo stared at the nativity scene in the large vestibule. Seeing the animals reminded her of Cap. Even though she had a new puppy, she still missed her former border collie.

On Christmas morning, Reverend Gavin delivered a masterful sermon that kept his congregation spellbound. When the service was over, he returned to the rectory to share a cup of cider with Jo. Just then the phone rang. Jo answered it.

"Hello, my name is Stephen Price-Walter," said the voice on the other end. "Do you own a dog named Cap?"

Jo could hardly speak while her mind raced with conflicting thoughts. *They found his body. No, they found him alive.* "Tell me, please, is he . . . is he . . ."

"He's alive, but barely."

Jo let out a scream. Covering the mouthpiece on the phone, she yelled, "Gavin! Gavin! Get on the extension. Someone found Cap. And he's alive!" Back on the phone, she frantically asked, "Where, how, when . . . ?"

"My wife, Saffron, and I have a border collie named Rosie," Stephen explained. "We had just started training her as a search-and-rescue dog. Earlier this morning, we took her out to Saint Bees Head. She came to a hole on the edge of the cliff and started barking like crazy. My wife and I ran over and looked into the hole. About five feet down, we spotted a border collie lying on the bottom. He was nothing but skin and bones and too weak to do anything but whimper. I climbed into the hole and felt him to make sure he didn't have any broken bones. He seemed in shock."

"This is so unbelievable!" exclaimed Gavin. "Our dog has been missing for eight weeks."

"Eight weeks?" said Stephen. "That's incredible."

"The weather here has been getting colder and frostier with each passing day," Gavin said. "How could he have lived without food and water for so long?"

"From what I could tell, he managed to survive on rainwater and a few dandelions that I found in the hole," Stephen replied. "He must have an astounding will to live, because I never would have believed any dog could have been trapped in there for two months and still be alive. Anyway, I lifted him out of the hole. He still had his collar and tags, so when I saw your phone number on a tag, I called you right away to give you the good news."

"Where are you now?" asked Gavin.

"We're still at Saint Bees. I'm calling from my mobile [cell phone]."

"Don't move. We'll be there in five minutes!"

Although they normally walked the two miles from their home to Saint Bees Head, the Walkers drove their car there. After they parked, they raced toward the cliff, where a young couple and border collie were standing over a prone black-and-white dog.

When the Walkers arrived, Jo dropped to her knees and began kissing Cap, cooing, "You're alive! You're alive!"

Cap wagged his tail feebly and was barely able to hold his head up long enough to lick Jo's face. "Oh, you're so skinny. You're half the size you were when we lost you. But you're alive. That's all that matters!"

Turning to Stephen and Saffron, Jo said, "We can't thank you enough for saving Cap."

"Don't thank us. Thank Rosie. She found him."

"Cap certainly would have died if it hadn't been for her," said Gavin. "I don't think Cap could have survived much longer."

"This is a Christmas miracle!" said Jo.

"In more ways than one," said Saffron. "You see, Rosie was born exactly a year ago—on Christmas Day."

The Walkers took Cap to the animal clinic for a complete examination. Although he was malnourished and dehydrated, the dog made a full recovery. But his owners kept him on a long leash. As for Gaspar, the "replacement dog," Cap and the puppy quickly became close friends.

About the Author

Allan Zullo is the author of more than ninety nonfiction books on subjects ranging from sports and the supernatural to history and animals.

He has written the bestselling Haunted Kids series, published by Scholastic, which are filled with chilling stories based on, or inspired by, documented cases from the files of ghost hunters. Allan also has introduced Scholastic readers to the Ten True Tales series, about people who have met the challenges of dangerous, sometimes life-threatening, situations. In addition, he has authored two books about the real-life experiences of kids during the Holocaust — *Survivors: True Stories of Children in the Holocaust* and *Heroes of the Holocaust: True Stories of Rescues by Teens.*

Allan, the grandfather of four and the father of two grown daughters, lives with his wife, Kathryn, on a mountainside near Asheville, North Carolina. To learn more about the author, visit his Web site at www.allanzullo.com.